FUTURE
English for Results

4

TESTS and TEST PREP
with **Exam***View*® *Assessment Suite*

Wendy Pratt Long
Kathleen Smith

Series Consultants
Beatriz B. Díaz
Ronna Magy
Federico Salas-Isnardi

PEARSON
Longman

Future 4 Tests and Test Prep

Staff credits: The people who made up the *Future 4 Tests and Test Prep* team, representing editorial, production, design, and manufacturing, are: Jennifer Adamec, Rhea Banker, Nancy Blodgett, Aerin Csigay, Nancy Flaggman, Irene Frankel, Katherine Keyes, Linda Moser, Barbara Sabella, Julie Schmidt, and Loretta Steeves.
Cover design: Rhea Banker
Cover photo: Kathy Lamm/Getty Images
Text composition: TSI Graphics
Text font: Minion Regular
Text design: Barbara Sabella

ISBN-13: 978-0-13-240919-3
ISBN-10: 0-13-240919-4

PEARSON LONGMAN ON THE WEB

Pearsonlongman.com offers online resources for teachers and students. Access our Companion Websites, our online catalog, and our local offices around the world.

Visit us at **www.pearsonlongman.com**.

Printed in the United States of America
7 18

Contents

Introduction

Welcome to *Future 4 Tests and Test Prep.* This package (containing a book, an audio CD, and a CD-ROM) provides all the assessment tools you need:

- The **Test Prep** section at the beginning of the book contains test-taking strategy worksheets and a sample unit test. These pages are photocopiable.
- The **Printed Unit Tests** in the book, also photocopiable, test students' mastery of the content presented in the Student Book units. The audio CD accompanies these tests.
- The **Exam***View*® *Assessment Suite* CD-ROM, found in the same envelope as the audio CD, offers a wealth of additional ways to assess students. Teachers can create their own unique tests. They can also print or customize already prepared unit tests in addition to midterm and final tests.

Test Prep

Test-Taking Strategy Worksheets

Many adult ESL students are unfamiliar with standardized tests. The Test Prep section contains reproducible worksheets that will prepare students for both the printed unit tests in this book and for any standardized tests they may have to take, such as the CASAS Life and Work Series. You will find the following worksheets on pages viii–x:

- How to Use an Answer Sheet
- Practice Questions for Standardized Tests
- Test-Taking Strategies

You can distribute the worksheets to your class over a period of time (for example, one page a week). Alternatively, you can wait until students are close to the time they will be tested or post-tested and then go over all the material in one session.

Sample Unit Test

The Sample Unit Test gives students the opportunity to practice the kinds of questions they will answer in the Unit Tests. On pages xi–xviii you will find:

- Instructions for the Sample Unit Test
- Sample Unit Test
- Answer Key and Audio Script for the Sample Unit Test

To administer the Sample Unit Test:

- Go over the Instructions for the Sample Unit Test with your class.
- Make copies of the test and of the blank Answer Sheet on page 97. Distribute the copies to your students. Have them bubble in their test answers on the Answer Sheet.
- The audio for the sample listening questions can be found on the audio CD, Track 2. There are 10-second pauses after each conversation to allow students to respond to the questions.
- Check answers using the Answer Key and the Audio Script for the Sample Unit Test on page xviii.

The Sample Unit Test (with the exception of the grammar and writing sections) is similar in format and content to the CASAS Life and Work Reading and Listening Series tests, but not identical to them. The CASAS website (www.casas.org) offers additional information, such as practice test questions, that you may find useful.

Printed Unit Tests

There are 12 printed Unit Tests in this test book. They are designed to assess how well students have mastered the material presented in each unit of the Student Book. Each test contains the following sections:

- Listening
- Life Skills
- Grammar
- Reading
- Writing

The Listening, Life Skills, and Reading sections of the tests emulate the look and feel of the CASAS Life and Work Reading and Listening Series tests. All the sections use a multiple-choice format, modeling the format students will encounter in standardized tests.

Listening

The Listening section includes a variety of item types and is divided into three parts: Listening I, Listening II, and Listening III.

Students listen to test items and look at the answer choices on the test page.

In **Listening I**, students hear a short conversation and have to answer a comprehension question about that conversation.

In **Listening II**, students hear part of a short conversation, and they have to choose the appropriate response to continue the conversation.

In **Listening III**, students hear a conversation. They then hear three sentences about the conversation and have to choose which sentence is true.

The directions and the answer choices appear on the Listening test page. This is different from the CASAS test, where students are not given answer choices to look at. In other words, on the CASAS test, students bubble in their answers on the answer sheet, but they do not see the questions or answer choices in print. If your students need extra support, give them the Listening Test page when you distribute the test. But if you wish to emulate CASAS more closely, you should omit this page.

Life Skills

In the Life Skills section, students read falsalia, such as a résumé or map. They then answer comprehension questions about it. In Unit 3, the Life Skills test also includes listening items.

Grammar

Students are asked to complete short conversations that contain examples of the grammar points presented in the unit.

Reading

Students read short articles or stories that reflect the grammar and themes covered in the unit and then answer comprehension questions about them.

Writing

Students read paragraphs, letters, and other types of writing and answer questions that test their understanding of the writing skills presented in the unit.

Answer Keys and Audio Scripts

You will find an Answer Key and an Audio Script for each printed Unit Test at the back of this book. The Answer Key is an answer sheet with the correct answers for the test bubbled in. It also provides diagnostic information about each test question. The Audio Script includes the conversations and comprehension questions. The direction lines and answer choices, which are also recorded, appear only on the test page.

Administering and Scoring Printed Unit Tests

To administer a printed Unit Test:

- Find the test you want in this book and photocopy it.
- Decide whether or not you want students to look at the Listening page as they take the test (see the Listening section). Either include or omit the Listening page when you distribute the test.
- Make copies of the blank Answer Sheet on page 97 and distribute them to your students. Ask students to bubble in their test answers on the Answer Sheet.

- Start with the Listening section of the test. Locate the appropriate audio track on the audio CD. Note that each item of the Listening section has a separate track. We recommend that you play each track twice, pausing for 10 to 20 seconds between each play. This will approximate how listening is presented on standardized tests.
- Each 33-item test is designed to take 25 to 30 minutes to administer.

To score a printed Unit Test:
- Collect your students' bubbled-in Answer Sheets.
- Locate the Answer Key for the test at the back of this book. To create a scoring mask, photocopy the Answer Key and punch a hole in each bubbled-in answer. When you lay this scoring mask over a student's Answer Sheet, you can easily see if the student has bubbled in the correct answer. If the bubble is not filled in, then simply mark an X on the unmarked bubble with a colored pencil.
- Count the number of correctly bubbled-in answers on the student's Answer Sheet. Each correct answer is worth three points. To calculate a percentage score for your students, multiply the number of correct answers by three and add one point.

The Answer Key provides the objective that each item tests, along with the lesson and page number in the Student Book where the material was presented. If a student answers a particular item incorrectly, you will then know which competency the student has missed and/or in which lesson he or she may need further practice.

Exam*View*® Assessment Suite

The **Exam***View*® *Assessment Suite* can be used either to supplement the printed Unit Tests or in place of them. With **Exam***View*, you can create or customize your own tests for students. Alternatively, you can choose to simply print out Unit, Midterm, or Final tests that have already been prepared for you and administer them to your class.

For detailed information on how to install the **Exam***View* software and use it to create, customize, and print out tests, please refer to the *TO THE TEACHER* PDF located on the *Future 4* **Exam***View Assessment Suite* CD-ROM. The installation instructions in the back of the book will tell you how to find this document.

Exam*View* Unit Tests

The **Exam***View* unit tests have the same general structure as the printed Unit Tests in the book, with a series of multiple choice questions that test listening, life skills, grammar, reading, and writing skills. However, the **Exam***View* unit tests do not follow the CASAS testing format as closely as the printed Unit Tests do. Another difference is that there are two separate types of tests for each unit. The first is a Listening Test in PDF format. The Listening Tests are offered in PDF format to make them easier for teachers to administer. Students listen to longer conversations (similar to the listenings in the Student Book) and then answer comprehension questions about them.

The second type of test is an **Exam***View* Test, containing life skills, grammar, reading, and writing items.

Exam*View* Midterm and Final Tests

The **Exam***View* Midterm and Final Tests provide an objective, standardized way to assess all your students at the halfway point and at the end of the course. The tests have a total of 66 items each. The Midterm tests the content presented in Units 1–6 and the Final covers Units 7–12. As with the Unit Tests, the Listening Midterm and Final Tests are in PDF format, and life skills, grammar, reading, and writing items are in **Exam***View* question banks.

Administering and Scoring
ExamView Tests

To administer an **Exam**View Test:

- You can administer **Exam**View Tests via computer or simply print them out and distribute them to your students. (The Listening Tests, as noted above, can only be administered in print format.)

- Locate the appropriate PDFs and **Exam**View tests on the CD-ROM. For example, if you wanted to administer the tests for Unit 1, you would print out the Listening test PDF and the **Exam**View test for Unit 1. (Please refer to the *TO THE TEACHER* PDF for more information on how to select the PDFs or tests you need.)

- Distribute the tests to your students. (Note: the Answer Keys for the **Exam**View tests print out automatically at the end of the test. Make sure you do not distribute the Answer Key to your students along with the test!)

- If you are printing out tests for your students, make copies of the blank Answer Sheet on page 97. Distribute two copies to each student. One copy is for the Listening Test, and the other copy is for the **Exam**View Test.

- Start with the Listening Test. Play the appropriate audio tracks for the test. The audio is located on the same CD-ROM as the **Exam**View Software. It can be played on any CD player or computer with CD-playing software. Have students listen and fill in the correct number of bubbles on the first Answer Sheet (usually, for eight test items). Then collect the Listening Answer Sheets.

- Next, administer the **Exam**View test for the unit. Have students bubble in the second Answer Sheet. Collect the Answer Sheets when students are finished.

- Allow 25–30 minutes for students to complete the Listening Test and the **Exam**View test for each unit. Allow 50–60 minutes for a midterm or final.

To score an **Exam**View Test:

- Collect your students' bubbled-in Answer Sheets.

- Locate the Answer Keys for the test. The Answer Keys and Audio Script for each Listening test are in PDF format in the same folder as the listening test. The Answer Keys for the **Exam**View tests will print out automatically at the end of each test, as noted above.

- Count the number of correctly bubbled-in answers on each student's set of Answer Sheets. Add the scores of the Listening Test and the **Exam**View test together. Then score the **Exam**View Unit Tests as you would a printed Unit Test. For the 66-item Midterm or Final test, multiply the number of correct answers by 3, add 2 free points, and divide the result by 2 to get a percentage score.

You can find detailed diagnostic information about each test item in the Answer Keys, including the following:

- Level of difficulty (DIF)

- Reference (REF): Student Book level and unit being tested

- Learning objective (OBJ): the learning objective of the item (as found in the *Scope & Sequence*/Student Book unit lesson)

- National standard (NAT): the CASAS competency being tested, if applicable

- Skill (SKL): the skill being tested (listening, life skills, grammar, reading, or writing)

As with the printed Unit Test Answer Keys, you can use this diagnostic information to determine the competencies and/or lessons in which your students need more practice.

HOW TO USE AN ANSWER SHEET

For many tests, you use an Answer Sheet to mark, or bubble in, your answers. You must use a #2 pencil. You do not mark your answers on the test. A machine may score your answers. The machine reads and records the pencil marks on the Answer Sheet.

First, you need to fill in some personal information on the Answer Sheet.

Here is an example of the Answer Sheet in this book:

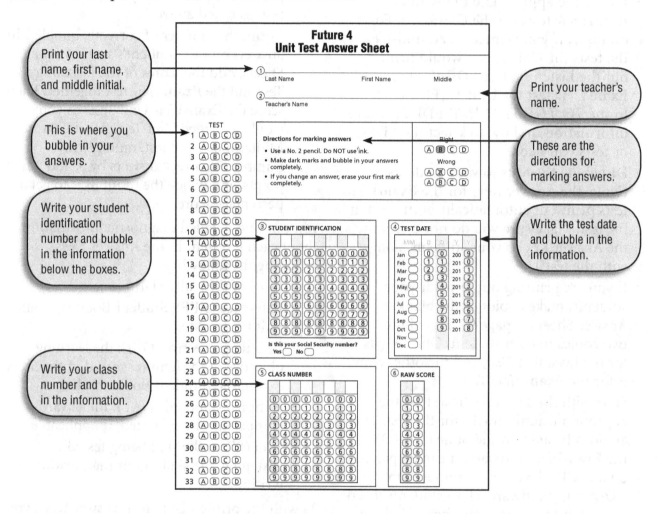

PRACTICE QUESTIONS FOR STANDARDIZED TESTS

Many standardized tests begin with a practice page. Here is an example of a practice page. Read through the questions below and make sure you understand how to answer them.

When you take a standardized test, find the practice page. It says *Practice.* Look for the practice answer box on the answer sheet. Use a pencil. Bubble in your answer. Ask the tester for help if you do not understand the directions. When the test begins, you are not allowed to talk. You cannot ask for or give help.

READING TEST

Practice

PREVIOUS EMPLOYER

EMPLOYER	ADDRESS	
Koll's	2200 E. Elm Street Monterey Park, CA 91754	
SUPERVISOR	PHONE #	May we contact? ☒ YES ☐ NO
Victor Santoro	(520) 555-9875	
STARTING POSITION	ENDING POSITION	
Clerk	Clerk	
DATES WORKED	JOB DUTIES	
03/15/08 – 04/28/10	worked cash register, customer service	
SALARY/WAGE	REASON FOR LEAVING	
$6.75/hr	wanted more hours	

APPLICANT SIGNATURE: _Li Chiu_   DATE: October 14, 2010

---

1. Why did Li Chiu leave his job with Koll's?

   A. He wanted a better salary.

   B. He wanted to work more hours.

   C. He was moving to a new address.

   D. He wanted to work at the cash register.

PRACTICE

1 (A) (B) (C) (D)
2 (A) (B) (C) (D)

TEST-TAKING STRATEGIES

Preparing to Take a Test

- Get a lot of sleep the night before the test.
- Eat a meal or snack before the test.
- Bring two sharpened #2 pencils.
- Bring a pencil eraser.
- Bring a ruler or a blank piece of paper.
- Arrive early to the testing room.
- Make sure you can easily see and hear the tester.
- Turn off your cell phone.
- Try to relax and do your best! Good luck!

Taking a Test

- As soon as you start a test section, look through the section to see how many questions there are.
- Don't spend too much time on any one question. If you don't know the answer, guess and then move on to the next item. You can circle the item number and come back to it at the end if you have time.
- For a listening section: Look at the answer choices for the question. Then listen to the directions and the question. Remember that for some questions, both questions and answer choices may be on the CD. You will hear the questions and the answer choices.
- For all other sections: Read the material. Read the question carefully. Read all the answer choices.
- Think: Which is the best answer? Look at the answer choices again. Eliminate answers you know are not correct.
- Choose the best answer.
- Make sure you mark your answer on the correct line on the answer sheet. Use a ruler to help you, or use a blank piece of paper to cover the lines below the line you are working on.
- Check each time that you bubble in the circle on the correct line for the question you are answering.
- Do not change the first answer you mark unless you are sure that it is wrong.
- Erase completely any answers you have changed. Fill in only ONE answer on each line. Erase all extra marks on your answer sheet.
- When you finish, if there is time, always recheck your answers.
- If you cannot answer many questions, it is OK. Raise your hand. Tell the tester. You may be excused from taking the rest of the test.

Test Prep: Sample Unit Test

INSTRUCTIONS FOR THE SAMPLE UNIT TEST

This sample test is like the Unit Tests in this book. It has Listening, Life Skills, Grammar, Reading, and Writing questions. Follow the directions carefully.

Listening Section

All the questions in the Listening section have three answer choices. Here are examples of the three types of listening questions:

Listening I: You listen to a conversation and choose the correct answer to a question about it. You will hear the question both before and after the conversation.

You will hear: What does the woman want to do?

> **F:** *I need to make an appointment with Dr. Chang.*
> **M:** *OK. When would you like to come in?*
> **F:** *Can I come in next Tuesday morning?*
>
> What does the woman want to do?
>
> A. She wants to see the doctor on Tuesday.
> B. She wants a job at a doctor's office.
> C. She wants to cancel an appointment.

The correct answer is A.

Listening II: You listen to the first part of a conversation and choose what the person will say next.

You will hear: **F:** *Want to go to the movies tonight?*
M: *Sorry. I have to work late tonight.*

> A. OK. Let's meet at 6:00.
> B. That's a really good movie.
> C. Too bad. How about tomorrow night?

The correct answer is C.

Listening III: You listen to a conversation and choose which sentence about it is true.

You will hear: **F:** *When did you start working at Al's Electronics?*
M: *Three years ago. I worked one year as a stock clerk and then I became a sales assistant.*

> Which sentence is true?
>
> A. The man worked in an electronics store for one year.
> B. The man was a stock clerk before he was a sales assistant.
> C. The man is working as a stock clerk now.

The correct answer is B.

Life Skills Section

The questions in the Life Skills sections have four answer choices. You read a short piece of information, such as a form, label, or map. You then answer questions about the information.

Grammar Section

The questions in the Grammar section have three answer choices. You read a short conversation and choose the correct answer to complete the conversation.

Reading Section

The questions in the Reading section have four answer choices. You read a short passage and then answer questions about the passage.

Writing Section

The questions in the Writing section have four answer choices. You read a paragraph, letter, or other type of writing and then answer questions about it.

LISTENING I

(Track 2) You will hear a question. Then you will hear a conversation. After that, you will hear the question again and three choices. What is the correct answer: A, B, or C?

1. A. one year
   B. two years
   C. three years

LISTENING II

You will hear the first part of a conversation. To finish the conversation, listen and choose the correct answer: A, B, or C.

2. A. Do you think I'm getting migraines?
   B. I've been taking some over-the-counter medicine.
   C. For about three weeks now.

LISTENING III

You will hear a conversation. Then you will hear three sentences. Which sentence is true: A, B, or C?

3. A. The man isn't going to attend the meeting.
   B. The man is going to attend the meeting.
   C. The man might attend the meeting.

LIFE SKILLS

Read. What is the correct answer: A, B, C, or D?

Current Charges	Amount
Customer charge 30 Days	4.93
Gas and Electricity Charges	140.07
Taxes and Fees	4.78
Total gas charges (Including taxes and fees)	149.78
Total Amount Now Due	**149.78**

Current Amount Past Due if not paid by Nov 30, 2010. A late charge of $5.00 may apply.

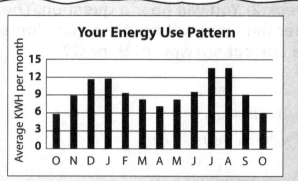

Your Energy Use Pattern

ENERGY SAVING TIP To save on your heating bill, set the thermostat lower. If you lower the thermostat slowly, over a few weeks, you will get used to the lower temperature.

Special DiscountYou may be eligible for California Alternate Rates for Energy (CARE) program. For more information and to request an application, please call 1-800-772-5050.

4. How much does the customer owe the electric company?
   A. $4.93
   B. $140.07
   C. $4.78
   D. $149.78

5. In which month did the customer use the most electricity?
   A. April
   B. August
   C. October
   D. December

GRAMMAR

Complete each conversation. What is the correct answer: A, B, or C?

6. **A:** I'm planning to go to school this fall.

   B: What courses _____ to take?

   A. will you

   B. you're going

   C. are you going

7. **A:** Have you ever _____ a computer class?

   B: Yes. I took a class at night last year.

   A. taken

   B. taking

   C. take

READING

Read. What is the correct answer: A, B, C, or D?

Min-Ji Lee came to the United States with almost no money and with very little English. Today she is the owner of a popular toy store, Min-Ji's Magic House. Min-Ji achieved her goal through hard work and creative thinking. Min-Ji's father was a carpenter in Korea, and he had taught her how to work with wood. So, when Min-Ji first arrived in the United States, she got a job at a furniture factory. She worked long hours to save money, and she took English classes on the weekends. Min-Ji enjoyed her job, but she wanted something more. One day, she realized that the factory was throwing out a lot of extra, small pieces of wood. Min-Ji had an idea. She got permission from her manager to take some of the wood home. At home, she used the wood to create a child's toy. She gave the toy to a friend's child. Her friend liked the toy and encouraged Min-Ji to make more. Soon, Min-Ji realized she had enough money to quit her job and pursue her dream of owning her own business. Five years ago, she opened her first store. Min-Ji's Magic House is a great success. Min-Ji plans to open a second store soon. She says, "My father taught me carpentry, but he also taught me something else. He taught me to have a dream and to follow it."

8. What is the main idea of the story?

   A. Min-Ji learned carpentry from her father in Korea.

   B. Min-Ji achieved her dream through hard work and creativity.

   C. Min-Ji took English classes on the weekends.

   D. Min-Ji had to save up a lot of money to start her business.

9. What was Min-Ji's first job in the United States?

   A. She was an assistant in a toy store.

   B. She was a carpenter in her father's store.

   C. She was a toy designer working at home.

   D. She was a furniture-maker in a factory.

10. Based on the information in the story, what inference can you make?

   A. Min-Ji works harder now than she did in the past.

   B. Min-Ji enjoys making toys more than making furniture.

   C. Min-Ji did not have a good relationship with her father.

   D. Min-Ji's friend gave her money to help her start her business.

WRITING

Manuel Lopez
1520 N. Calle Verde
Tucson, AZ 85745

August 25, 2010

Barbara Weiss, Manager
Arnold's Steak House
2880 E. Broadway
Tucson, AZ 85701

Dear Ms. Weiss:

Thank you for the interview on Monday for the chef position at Arnold's Steak House. I enjoyed meeting you and learning more about the restaurant.

As I mentioned during the interview, I have experience managing a kitchen in a fast-paced restaurant. At my previous job, I worked long hours and was usually not paid overtime.

_____. Please call me at (520) 555-8958 if you have any more questions
    12.
about my qualifications. I look forward to speaking with you soon.

Sincerely,

Manuel Lopez

Manuel Lopez

11. Which sentence should Manuel *not* include in the letter?

  A. I enjoyed meeting you and learning more about the restaurant.

  B. I have experience managing a kitchen in a fast-paced restaurant.

  C. At my previous job, I worked long hours and was usually not paid overtime.

  D. Please call me at (520) 555-8958 if you have any questions about my qualifications.

12. Which sentence should Manuel use to begin the last paragraph of the letter?

  A. I think I would be a good addition to your staff.

  B. I would like to start working on September 10.

  C. I plan to take more culinary classes in the fall.

  D. Please tell me if I will get the job.

ANSWER KEY AND AUDIO SCRIPT FOR THE SAMPLE UNIT TEST

Answer Key

1. B	7. A
2. C	8. B
3. C	9. D
4. D	10. B
5. B	11. C
6. C	12. A

Audio Script *(Track 2)*

LISTENING I

1. How long has the woman worked for the store in Linden?

   M: So, you've been an assistant manager for three years?

   F: Well, I was an assistant manager at Shop N Shop in Union for one year. And then I moved to the Linden store. I've been there for two years. So, three years all together, yes.

   M: OK, great. Have you ever worked at night?

   How long has the woman worked for the store in Linden?

LISTENING II

2. **M:** Hello, Mrs. Martinez. I'm Dr. Baker. I'm sorry to hear that you've been having headaches.

   F: Thank you. They seem to be getting worse. I feel dizzy and nauseous.

   M: How long have you been having these symptoms?

LISTENING III

3. **F:** I'm going to the meeting at City Hall tonight. They're going to talk about putting a traffic light on the corner of Elm and 5th Streets.

   M: Oh, good. That intersection is terrible. There are always accidents there.

   F: I know. They really need to do something.

   M: What time is the meeting? I'd like to go.

   Which sentence is true?

Unit 1 Test

🎧 LISTENING I

(Tracks 3–5) You will hear a question. Then you will hear a conversation. After that, you will hear the question again and three choices. What is the correct answer: A, B, or C?

1. A. his routine
   B. his goals
   C. his work experience

2. A. drive his car
   B. take the bus
   C. read and relax

3. A. She usually works in the mornings.
   B. She usually works in the evenings.
   C. She usually works with Michelle.

🎧 LISTENING II

(Tracks 6–7) You will hear the first part of a conversation. To finish the conversation, listen and choose the correct answer: A, B, or C.

4. A. Yes, I used to work in a hotel.
   B. Yes, I'm looking for a job now.
   C. Yes, I'm going to start my job next week.

5. A. I used to drive a truck.
   B. I drive a truck every day.
   C. I'm going to get a college degree.

🎧 LISTENING III

(Tracks 8–10) You will hear a conversation. Then you will hear three sentences. Which sentence is true: A, B, or C?

6. A. The man lives in the city.
   B. The man has a big apartment.
   C. The man doesn't have any children.

7. A. The woman usually watches TV during the week.
   B. The woman is going to watch TV tonight.
   C. The woman doesn't usually relax during the week.

8. A. The women take classes together.
   B. Olga is taking classes now.
   C. Olga will start school in the future.

LIFE SKILLS

Read the next page and answer these questions. What is the correct answer: A, B, C, or D?

9. What does Teresa need to do?

   A. complete the application and send it with $25 and her official transcripts

   B. ask for $25 to be returned to her after she sends in her application

   C. send $25 and her official transcripts before she completes the application

   D. send the application in the spring in 2011

10. What information does the application ask for?

   A. the address of the applicant's last school

   B. the date the applicant started high school

   C. when the applicant wants to begin studying

   D. records of the applicant's college or university work

11. Which is true about the *Optional* section of the application?

   A. Teresa can choose whether or not to complete that section.

   B. Teresa should check all the boxes in that section.

   C. Teresa is required to complete that section.

   D. Teresa has to complete that section if she wasn't born in the United States.

12. What does Teresa do now?

   A. She doesn't have a job.

   B. She's an assistant manager.

   C. She's a waitress.

   D. She works at La Casita Amarilla.

FORWARD TECHNICAL SCHOOL

www.forwardtechnicalschool.com
210-555-4949
Office of Admissions
2000 Central Avenue
San Antonio, TX 78202

Submit the following with your completed application:
- $25 nonrefundable application fee
- official high school transcripts

Applying for
☐ Fall 20_____   ☒ Spring 20 **11**_____   ☐ Summer 20_____

APPLICANT'S INFORMATION

Name **Fernandez**   **Teresa**_____
     (last)   (first)   (middle)

Address **218 Nogales Rd. San Antonio**   **TX**   **78201**
      (street)   (city)   (state)   (zip)

Phone **210-555-0711**   E-mail **tfernandez@getmymail.com**

Date of birth ___**01/23/89**___   Gender ☐ male ☒ female
           (MM/DD/YY)

PERSONAL

Citizenship   ☒ United States   ☐ Green card holder   ☐ Other

Native Language   ☐ English ☒ Other **bilingual in English and Spanish**

OPTIONAL

Forward Technical School is an equal opportunity institution. This information is requested to comply with federal law and will not affect consideration of your application.

Ethnicity   ☐ African American, Black
               ☐ American Indian / Alaskan
               ☐ Asian or Pacific Islander
               ☐ Hispanic or Latino White
               ☐ White, Non-Hispanic
               ☐ Other or prefer not to answer

EDUCATION

High School Attended **Dorado High School**_____

☒ Graduated **05/08**___   ☐ Passed GED Test: _____
        (MM/YY)   (MM/YY)

Colleges Attended _____

☐ Associate's Degree ☐ Bachelor's Degree ☐ Some Credits

WORK HISTORY (Begin with most recent employer.)

Employer **Café de los Angeles**   Job Title **assistant manager**_____

City and State **San Antonio, TX**   Dates **02/09** to **present**_____

Employer **Café de los Angeles**   Job Title **waitress**_____

City and State **San Antonio, TX**   Dates **03/07** to **02/09**

Employer **La Casita Amarilla**   Job Title **hostess**_____

City and State **San Antonio, TX**   Dates **08/05** to **03/07**

Applicant's Signature _____ Date _____

GRAMMAR

Complete each conversation. What is the correct answer: A, B, or C?

13. A: What time is their lunch break?
  B: They usually _____ it at 12:30.

    A. take
    B. taking
    C. are taking

14. A: Where's Abdi?
  B: In his bedroom. He _____ his application for the technical school.

    A. completes
    B. completing
    C. 's completing

15. A: Is your daughter making plans for after high school?
  B: Yes, she is. She _____ to study at a culinary school in the fall.

    A. is wanting
    B. wants
    C. want

16. A: What _____ these days?
  B: Oh, he's busy. He has a job, and he's taking classes.

    A. is Jordi doing
    B. Jordi does
    C. does Jordi

17. A: Is _____ to the supervisor about her schedule?
  B: Yes. She's in his office right now.

    A. Zina talks
    B. Zina talk
    C. Zina talking

18. A: What are your plans for after graduation?
  B: I _____ classes at the community college.

    A. going to
    B. 'm going to take
    C. taking

19. A: I really need to finish this report today.
  B: I'm not too busy. I _____ help you with it after lunch.

    A. 'll
    B. going to
    C. 'm going

20. **A:** You need to finish your homework.

   B: I know. I _____ it later.

   A. 'll do

   B. 'm going to

   C. doing

21. **A:** Are you busy tonight?

   B: Yeah. Monica and David _____ over to my apartment for dinner.

   A. will

   B. are coming

   C. come

22. **A:** Felipe _____ the career center at his school tomorrow.

   B: That's great. He can get a lot of good information there.

   A. going to visit

   B. is going to visit

   C. visiting

23. **A:** My parents didn't _____ a lot of time to spend with us when we were young.

   B: But now your family spends a lot of time together.

   A. had

   B. has

   C. have

24. **A:** _____ to be a doctor when you were a kid?

   B: No. I wanted to be a soccer player.

   A. Did you want

   B. You want

   C. You used

25. **A:** Did you know that Fatik graduated from college?

   B: Yeah. _____ his bachelor's degree last year.

   A. He didn't

   B. He gets

   C. He got

26. **A:** Jing-Wei just moved to Los Angeles.

   B: Yeah. _____ live in Seattle.

   A. She used

   B. She used to

   C. Did she

27. **A:** Mr. Feng didn't _____ on weekends.

   B: I know, but he changed his schedule.

   A. use to work

   B. used to work

   C. use to

READING I

Read. What is the correct answer: A, B, C, or D?

MEET A COMMUNITY MEMBER

Hard Work, Big Changes

When Makeda Dibo decides to make a change, she works hard to reach her goal.

Makeda Dibo's life now is very different than it was five years ago. That was when Makeda and her husband moved to the United States from Ethiopia. Makeda didn't speak much English. She needed her husband's help a lot, and she couldn't get a job. So Makeda decided to make a change. She signed up for an English class at Silver Crest Adult School. She went to class every day. She did her homework and studied at night. Makeda practiced speaking English whenever she could. She learned quickly.

Then Makeda set a goal: to get a college degree. She applied to Princetown Community College, and she was accepted. Now she is studying education there. She's going to graduate next year, and then she'll look for a job. Her goal is to get a job teaching English. She wants to help other people make changes in their lives.

---

28. What is the main idea of this story?

    A. Makeda is thinking about making some changes in the future.

    B. Makeda's husband wants her to make changes in her life.

    C. Makeda's husband sets goals for her.

    D. Makeda works hard to make big changes.

29. What does Makeda do now?

    A. She works at Silver Crest Adult School.

    B. She's helping her husband learn English.

    C. She's a student at a community college.

    D. She's studying English at an adult school.

READING II

Read. What is the correct answer: A, B, C, or D?

Dulce Navarro loves working with children. For five years she was a child-care worker in Lima, Peru. After she moved to the United States, she got a job selling tickets at Snowy Hills Movie Theater. She has been working at the movie theater since then. Dulce likes her job, but she would like to work with children again. Her dream is to be a teacher. Eventually she wants to become a teacher of preschool children. But first she needs to get a degree. Now she's looking at different programs online and at the community college near her. She plans to choose a program and send in her application by the end of the month.

30. What did Dulce used to do?

    A. She used to study at a community college.

    B. She used to sell tickets at a movie theater.

    C. She used to take classes online.

    D. She used to be a child-care worker.

31. What is Dulce's long-term goal?

    A. to start an online program

    B. to be a teacher

    C. to choose a program where she can get her degree

    D. to send in her application

WRITING

Read. What is the correct answer: A, B, C, or D?

Flaviu Arcos's Life	
1950	came to the United States got a job with a furniture maker
1951	had idea to open his own furniture store
1953	studied English
1955	married my grandmother
1957	had a son (my father)
1958	started to work a second job
1970	quit other jobs and opened a furniture store
1975	moved furniture store to a bigger space
1980	opened second furniture store
present	still works at his stores every day

A Great Teacher

Flaviu Arcos is my grandfather and my role model. I've learned a lot from his example. My grandfather came to the United States from Romania when he was fifteen years old. His first goal was to get a job. A month after he arrived, he started working for a Romanian furniture maker. He worked hard, and he learned the business quickly. It turned out that my grandfather was very good at furniture making, and he really enjoyed it. So it made sense that he had the idea to open his own furniture store one day. My grandfather knew that he had a lot more to learn before he was ready for that.

32. According to the timeline, which sentence should come next?

A. He got married to my grandmother when he was twenty.

B. Then he started to work a second job.

C. Since he only spoke Romanian, he decided to study English.

D. Twenty years later, he opened a furniture store.

33. According to the timeline, what should the writer describe last?

A. the opening of the second store

B. moving the store to a bigger space

C. his grandfather's first job

D. his grandfather's work at the stores now

Unit 2 Test

🔘 LISTENING I

(Tracks 11–13) **You will hear a question. Then you will hear a conversation. After that, you will hear the question again and three choices. What is the correct answer: A, B, or C?**

1. A. his references
    B. his education
    C. his work experience

2. A. She wants to start taking classes.
    B. She wants to work in an office.
    C. She wants to find an assistant.

3. A. go to Brazil
    B. finish her degree
    C. start taking classes at night

🔘 LISTENING II

(Tracks 14–15) **You will hear the first part of a conversation. To finish the conversation, listen and choose the correct answer: A, B, or C.**

4. A. I can use a computer, and I'm very organized.
    B. I'm very excited about this job.
    C. I plan to work during the day and study at night.

5. A. One year.
    B. Last year.
    C. I'm happy there.

🔘 LISTENING III

(Tracks 16–18) **You will hear a conversation. Then you will hear three sentences. Which sentence is true: A, B, or C?**

6. A. The man doesn't have a job.
    B. The man works in a factory.
    C. The man is a dishwasher.

7. A. The woman isn't interested in fashion.
    B. The woman likes fashion.
    C. The woman works at a clothing store.

8. A. The woman is looking for a job.
    B. The woman works at an employment agency.
    C. The woman doesn't have a résumé.

LIFE SKILLS

Read the next page and answer these questions. What is the correct answer: A, B, C, or D?

9. What job does Gabriela want?

   A. assistant manager of a hotel

   B. hotel desk clerk

   C. restaurant manager

   D. volunteer in a soup kitchen

10. What kind of information is included in the *Related Experience* section?

    A. names of people who can recommend Gabriela for the job

    B. Gabriela's future goals

    C. details about the job Gabriela wants

    D. some of Gabriela's job responsibilities

11. What does Gabriela do now?

    A. She works in a restaurant.

    B. She works in a hotel.

    C. She's a volunteer.

    D. She's a student.

12. What does Gabriela's experience *not* include?

    A. managing people

    B. working with customers

    C. working as an assistant manager in a hotel

    D. organizing records

GABRIELA FLORES

2198 14th St., Apt. 6C, Brooklyn, NY 11235

718-555-7369   gflores@nycmail.com

OBJECTIVE

To work as an assistant manager of a hotel

RELATED EXPERIENCE

Hotel Desk Clerk   July 2008–present

Covington Hotel, New York, NY

- Make reservations for guests by phone and in person
- Organize and maintain reservations and other records
- Provide excellent customer service, including responding to customer questions, requests, and complaints

Restaurant Manager   August 2005–July 2008

Prime 100 Restaurant, Brooklyn, NY

- Managed crew of 10 people in busy environment
- Hired and trained new employees
- Organized and maintained records of orders and supplies

Volunteer   July 2007–July 2008

Life Bread Soup Kitchen, Brooklyn, NY

- Worked with partner to plan and prepare weekly meal for 25–30 people

EDUCATION

Certificate in Hospitality Administration   April 2008

Capitol Technical School, Albany, NY

References available upon request.

GRAMMAR

Complete each conversation. What is the correct answer: A, B, or C?

13. **A:** What did the career counselor ask you?

B: Well, first she wanted _____ about my personal qualities and skills.

  A. to know

  B. know

  C. knowing

14. **A:** How was the job fair?

B: It was good. I recommend _____ if you're looking for a job.

  A. go

  B. going

  C. to go

15. **A:** Would you consider _____ for a job?

B: That's a good question. It would depend a lot on the job.

  A. moving

  B. have moved

  C. to move

16. **A:** I couldn't go to the meeting today. Did I miss anything?

B: Well, we decided _____ the schedule for next week.

  A. change

  B. changing

  C. to change

17. **A:** Sally is thinking about a career in health care.

B: That's great. She really enjoys _____ care of people.

  A. to take

  B. taking

  C. took

18. **A:** How was your meeting at the employment agency?

B: Great. I'm really _____ getting a job now.

  A. excited

  B. excited about

  C. exciting

19. **A:** I think Malina would be a good manager.

B: You know, you're right. She's good at _____ people.

  A. motivate

  B. to motivate

  C. motivating

20. **A:** Your daughter just graduated from high school, didn't she?

B: Yes. She's planning on _____ to college in the fall.

  A. she's going

  B. going

  C. to go

21. A: A lot of students are worried about _____ jobs after graduation.

B: I know. Many of them need to start earning money as soon as they can.

A. find
B. have found
C. finding

22. A: Thanks for _____ me about the job opening at the flower shop.

B: No problem. I think you'd be good at it.

A. telling
B. to tell
C. tell

23. A: How long _____ a manager at Neighborhood Harvest Market?

B: Since 2007. It's a good job, and he's very happy there.

A. was Jin
B. Jin was
C. has Jin been

24. A: Did you use to work for the Primus Company?

B: Yes, I did. _____ there from 2006 to 2008. Then I got my job here.

A. I worked
B. I have worked
C. Have I worked

25. A: How's Tom's job search going?

B: OK. _____ his résumé, and now he's ready to send it out.

A. He's writing
B. He has written
C. Did he write

26. A: How was your interview yesterday?

B: Good. The interviewer _____ a lot of questions, but it went well.

A. asked
B. asking
C. has asked

27. A: Where are Manny and Juan?

B: They're still at the office. They _____ their work yet.

A. didn't
B. haven't finished
C. not finished

READING I
Read. What is the correct answer: A, B, C, or D?

Hector studied at Valley Culinary School for two years. He learned excellent food preparation skills. After graduation, he wanted to find a job. He looked at the job ads in the newspaper. He applied to several jobs, but he never heard back from any employers. Hector also told his friends he was looking for a job. A friend's sister, Victoria, owned a restaurant. Hector's friend gave Hector his sister's phone number. Hector called Victoria, and they talked. A few weeks later, Victoria called Hector. She said one of her workers had quit and she needed a new line cook. Hector went to the restaurant for an interview. The next day, Victoria offered him the job. It wasn't a high-level position, but that was OK with Hector. He accepted the job immediately.

28. What was Hector's goal after graduation?

A. to get a job

B. to get a high-level position

C. to go back to school

D. to gain food preparation skills

29. What did Hector do before he was offered the job?

A. He completed an application.

B. He got work experience.

C. He sent his résumé.

D. He had an interview.

READING II

Read. What is the correct answer: A, B, C, or D?

Creating, Expanding, and Using Your Network

Many career experts say that the most successful way to find a job is by networking. Networking is talking to people. So when you're looking for a job, let people know. Tell your friends, family, and neighbors. Talk to your classmates, teachers, counselors, and coworkers.

When you network, you can ask people about job openings, but you should also ask for their help and suggestions. Ask if they know anyone in the field you're interested in or if they know how you might learn more about the job you want. Get the name and phone number of anyone they think might be able to help. Then call that person and ask for some information.

In this way, you might not get a job offer immediately, but you might meet a person who can eventually help you get a job. Remember, every time you talk to someone, your network gets bigger, and you increase your chances of finding a job.

30. What is the purpose of this article?

A. to network

B. to show how networking helped one person find a job

C. to suggest different ways to find a job

D. to explain what networking is and how to do it

31. According to the article, which statement is true?

A. If you network, you'll probably get a job offer very quickly.

B. You should ask for people's help and suggestions when you network.

C. Even if you talk to a lot of people, it probably won't help you find a job.

D. You should only talk to people who you think can help you find a job.

WRITING

Read. What is the correct answer: A, B, C, or D?

431 21st St., Apt. 4B
Denver, CO 80203
303-555-1976
melissatran@denvermail.com

June 8, 2009

Simon Richards
Clean Smile Dental Group
10982 Franklin Blvd.
Denver, CO 80204

Dear Mr. Richards,

I am writing in response to the ad in The Denver Post on June 7, 2009 for a dental assistant job. The position is an excellent fit with my interests, training, and experience. I've enclosed my résumé for your review.

I recently completed my education at Mountain Technical School and received a certificate from their dental assistant program. I am motivated, detail-oriented, and good with people. I have developed strong professional skills in my current job as a customer service assistant. I work full time at that job, so my schedule is very busy.

I'm familiar with your office, and I would love to be a member of your team. I can be available for an interview at any time that is convenient for you. Thank you for considering my application.

Sincerely,
Melissa Tran

Melissa Tran

Enclosure

32. What is the enclosure with this letter?

A. a cover letter

B. the ad from *The Denver Post*

C. Melissa's résumé

D. Melissa's certificate from Mountain Technical School

33. Which sentence should Melissa *not* include in the cover letter?

A. I am writing in response to your ad for a dental assistant in *The Denver Post* on March 19, 2009.

B. I recently completed my education at Palm Technical School and received a certificate from their dental assistant program.

C. I am motivated, detail-oriented, and good with people.

D. I work full time at that job, so my schedule is very busy.

Unit 3 Test

LISTENING I

(Tracks 19–20) You will hear a question. Then you will hear a conversation. After that, you will hear the question again and three choices. What is the correct answer: A, B, or C?

1. A. an issue in the community
   B. his feelings about the neighborhood
   C. a cultural festival

2. A. a better car
   B. a place to park his car
   C. more public transportation

LISTENING II

(Tracks 21–22) You will hear the first part of a conversation. To finish the conversation, listen and choose the correct answer: A, B, or C.

3. A. Our house is very relaxing.
   B. I'm frustrated by some of the problems.
   C. The neighboring town is Oakdale.

4. A. It's pretty amazing.
   B. The mayor encourages people to go downtown.
   C. Go south to get downtown.

LISTENING III

(Tracks 23–26) You will hear a conversation. Then you will hear three sentences. Which sentence is true: A, B, or C?

5. A. The man thinks the neighborhood is embarrassing.
   B. The man's sister embarrasses him.
   C. The man's sister feels embarrassed.

6. A. Mrs. Madison asked the police for help.
   B. Police want people to check on their neighbors.
   C. The woman is going to tell the police about Mrs. Madison.

7. A. The man doesn't want to go to the meeting.
   B. The man thinks they can change the community.
   C. The woman is frustrated with the community.

8. A. There's a problem with the roads.
   B. The community is fixing the potholes.
   C. There's a lot of trash on the roads.

⊘ LIFE SKILLS

(Track 27) Listen to the conversation about some community activities and places. Then answer the questions. What is the correct answer: A, B, or C?

9. A. 3:30 to 7:30
   B. 3:00 to 7:30
   C. 3:30 to 7:00

10. A. The activities have a low cost.
    B. All the activities are free.
    C. There is a small fee for some activities.

11. A. Go north on Orchard Street, then west on Bruce.
    B. Make a left on Orchard Street, and go west on Bruce.
    C. Go west on Orchard Street, then north on Bruce.

12. A. on Amber Drive
    B. on Sterling Street
    C. at 406 East Street

GRAMMAR

Complete each conversation. What is the correct answer: A, B, or C?

13. **A:** Are you looking forward to the party this weekend?

    B: Yeah, I'm _____ about it. I think it's going to be a lot of fun.

    A. exciting

    B. excited

    C. excite

14. **A:** Crime in our neighborhood is down since we formed the Neighborhood Watch.

    B: Wow. That's really _____. Keep up the good work!

    A. encouraged by

    B. encouraging

    C. encouraged

15. **A:** My boyfriend and I went shopping this weekend. It was so much fun.

    B: You're lucky. My husband is _____ shopping. He never goes with me.

    A. boring

    B. bored by

    C. bore

16. **A:** Did you go to the block party last weekend?

    B: Yes. I was _____ how many people were there.

    A. surprised at

    B. surprising to

    C. surprised with

17. **A:** How was the Spring Festival?

    B: Great! We were _____ at all the delicious food.

    A. amazed

    B. to amaze

    C. amazing

18. **A:** Do you like your new neighborhood?

    B: Yes, I do. But I wish _____ more parks nearby.

    A. there was

    B. there were

    C. there are

19. **A:** I wish people _____ trash on the ground in the park.

    B: I know. They should put their trash in garbage cans!

    A. didn't throw

    B. not throw

    C. won't throw

20. **A:** I wish everyone _____ about keeping our city clean.

    B: Me, too. It's frustrating when people don't take care of it.

    A. caring
    B. cares
    C. cared

21. **A:** How does Joe like his new job?

    B: He likes the job, but he wishes he _____ drive to work every day.

    A. has to
    B. didn't have to
    C. not have to

22. **A:** I wish I _____ more free time. I never have time to just relax.

    B: I know. I feel the same way.

    A. had
    B. have
    C. having

23. **A:** What kinds of safety tips did the police officer give the kids?

    B: Well, he told _____ ride their bikes at night.

    A. they don't
    B. they aren't
    C. them not to

24. **A:** What's the Community Council?

    B: It's a group that encourages residents _____ involved in community activities.

    A. to get
    B. get
    C. are getting

25. **A:** Did you talk to Linda today?

    B: Yes. She wants _____ her in the park this afternoon.

    A. I meet
    B. me to meet
    C. I'm meeting

26. **A:** The mayor's office urges residents _____ their doors unlocked.

    B: That's good advice.

    A. not to leave
    B. don't leave
    C. not leaving

27. **A:** Make sure Heather takes her cell phone with her today.

    B: I already reminded _____ it in her purse.

    A. she puts
    B. she put
    C. her to put

READING I

Read. What is the correct answer: A, B, C, or D?

When Graciela Chavez and her husband moved to Lincoln City, Graciela didn't speak English well. None of her neighbors spoke Spanish, so she didn't talk to people. She was very unhappy. One day Graciela saw a sign for an English class at the community center. Graciela began taking the class, and her English improved. She started to talk to her neighbors. It wasn't always easy, but Graciela got to know some of them. She learned that she and her neighbors were similar in a lot of ways. They had the same concerns about the run-down buildings in their community. One neighbor encouraged Graciela to join the community group. Graciela still doesn't speak English perfectly, but she's improving. Now she feels like she's part of her community. She's meeting people, and she's making a difference.

28. How does Graciela probably feel about her community now?

A. She probably feels the same about it as when she first arrived.

B. She probably feels more like an outsider than when she first arrived.

C. She probably likes it less than when she first arrived.

D. She probably likes it more than when she first arrived.

29. How are Graciela's neighbors similar to her?

A. They didn't speak English very well at first.

B. They are unhappy in Lincoln City.

C. They are worried about run-down buildings.

D. They are worried about the trash in the community.

READING II

Read. What is the correct answer: A, B, C, or D?

Chinese Cultural Festival

Come join us this Saturday from 11:00 A.M. to 9:00 P.M. for Jefferson City's annual Chinese Cultural Festival. This year the celebration will be held downtown in Taylor Park. The festival is free for everyone, and everyone is welcome.

There's something for everyone at this year's festival! Here are just some of the activities you can enjoy. See beautiful Chinese arts and crafts. Watch the cultural parade. Get your name translated into Chinese for free. Enjoy performances of traditional Chinese music and dancing. Learn about visiting China and what to see and do there. And, of course, bring your appetite— there will be lots of delicious Chinese food! Children and adults will enjoy this celebration of Chinese culture. Bring your family and come celebrate with us!

30. What is the purpose of this article?

   A. to tell about the success of the Chinese Cultural Festival

   B. to explain how this year's festival will be different from ones in past years

   C. to provide information about China

   D. to invite people to go to the Chinese Cultural Festival

31. What is the main idea of the second paragraph of this article?

   A. You can learn a lot about China at the festival.

   B. The festival will be fun for everyone.

   C. This year's festival will be better than last year's.

   D. People will really enjoy the traditional music and dancing.

WRITING

Read. What is the correct answer: A, B, C, or D?

A Barbecue to Remember

Last Labor Day, some of our neighbors had a barbecue. They invited my wife, our two sons, and me. At first we didn't know if we were going to go. My wife was tired from working all weekend, and I was very busy. But in the end, we decided to go, and we were really glad we did!

First of all, there were lots of fun activities.
_____
        (32.)

But there's another reason why the barbecue was great. My wife and I learned about some services available in our community. _____
                                    (33.)

32. Which sentence should be added to the second paragraph to give details about its main idea?

A. The food was really delicious.

B. I learned a lot about our neighborhood.

C. We met the family who lives across the street from us.

D. We played volleyball and soccer, and in the evening we danced.

33. Which sentence should be added to the third paragraph to give details about its main idea?

A. Someone explained why people celebrate Labor Day.

B. One neighbor told us about free after-school programs for kids.

C. Our neighbors taught us how to barbecue.

D. Our kids met the neighbors across the street, and now they're friends.

Unit 4 Test

LISTENING I

(Tracks 28–30) You will hear a question. Then you will hear a conversation. After that, you will hear the question again and three choices. What is the correct answer: A, B, or C?

1. A. make an appointment for her performance review
   B. follow safety procedures
   C. ask questions

2. A. get information about his vacation days
   B. find a calendar to plan his vacation
   C. pick his vacation days

3. A. fix the problems
   B. show the man the problems
   C. point at the man

LISTENING II

(Tracks 31–32) You will hear the first part of a conversation. To finish the conversation, listen and choose the correct answer: A, B, or C.

4. A. Yes, I do.
   B. No, we can't.
   C. No, we don't.

5. A. No, I got over it.
   B. No, I took it over.
   C. No, I put it together.

LISTENING III

(Tracks 33–35) You will hear a conversation. Then you will hear three sentences. Which sentence is true: A, B, or C?

6. A. The woman is reporting a problem.
   B. The woman is offering a solution.
   C. The woman is checking her understanding.

7. A. The doctor has the information.
   B. The man is going to give the information to the doctor.
   C. The doctor gave the man the information.

8. A. The man got hurt at work.
   B. The woman has to miss work.
   C. The woman has an injury.

LIFE SKILLS

Read the next page and answer these questions. What is the correct answer: A, B, C, or D?

9. Which of the following are employees allowed to do?

   A. work six hours of overtime in one week without their manager's approval

   B. work twelve hours of overtime in one week without their manager's approval

   C. work twelve hours of overtime in one week with their manager's approval

   D. work fifteen hours of overtime in one week with their manager's approval

10. Tamra began working at National Services six months ago. How many paid vacation days does she get this year?

    A. none

    B. five

    C. ten

    D. fifteen

11. What is the policy at National Services regarding New Year's Day?

    A. Employees don't work, but they don't get paid.

    B. Employees work, and they get paid for a regular workday.

    C. Employees work, and they get paid overtime.

    D. Employees don't work, but they get paid for a regular workday.

12. Look at the calendar. National Services employees got paid on December 3. When will they get paid next?

December						
SUN.	MON.	TUES.	WED.	THURS.	FRI.	SAT.
			1	2	3	4
5	6	7	8	9	10	11
12	13	14	15	16	17	18
19	20	21	22	23	24	25
26	27	28	29	30	31	

A. December 10

B. December 17

C. December 24

D. December 31

National Services

Employee Benefits Summary

OVERTIME

- The pay rate for overtime work is one and one-half times the employee's regular hourly rate. Employees are allowed to work a maximum of twelve hours of overtime per week. All overtime hours require a manager's approval.

PAID TIME OFF

- Employees are allowed a maximum of ten paid sick days per year. A doctor's note is required for any illness that causes an employee to miss three or more days of work.
- Paid vacation days are based on years of service with the company.

Employees who have worked at the company for	will receive
less than one year	5 paid vacation days per year.
1–5 years	10 paid vacation days per year.
6–10 years	15 paid vacation days per year.
11 years or more	20 paid vacation days per year.

- In addition to paid sick and vacation days, employees are allowed two paid personal days per year.
- If possible, notify your manager of any planned vacation or personal days at least five days in advance.
- National Services is closed for the following federal holidays: New Year's Day, Martin Luther King Jr. Day, Washington's Birthday, Memorial Day, Independence Day, Labor Day, Columbus Day, Veterans' Day, Thanksgiving, and Christmas. These are paid holidays; employees will be paid for each of these days as a regular workday.

PAYROLL

- National Services pays employees biweekly.

GRAMMAR

Complete each conversation. What is the correct answer: A, B, or C?

13. **A:** How's Fran's new job?
    B: Good. There's a lot to learn, but she's picking _____ quickly.
    A. up it
    B. it up
    C. (Both A and B are correct.)

14. **A:** Do you have to talk in front of a lot of people at work?
    B: Yeah. I used to be so scared! But now I'm getting _____.
    A. over my fear
    B. my fear over
    C. (Both A and B are correct.)

15. **A:** Is Mr. Graham still working in the store?
    B: Yes, but his daughter is going to take _____ next year so he can retire.
    A. the business over
    B. over the business
    C. (Both A and B are correct.)

16. **A:** The managers are going to put _____ to fix the problem.
    B: That's good news. When will it be finished?
    A. together a plan
    B. a plan together
    C. (Both A and B are correct.)

17. **A:** How do you like your job?
    B: I like it, and I really like the people I work with. I know I can count _____ to help me if I need them.
    A. on my coworkers
    B. my coworkers on
    C. (Both A and B are correct.)

18. **A:** I'm on the schedule for Friday morning, but I can't work that shift.
    B: _____ trade shifts with someone?
    A. Can't you
    B. You don't
    C. Haven't you

19. **A:** Didn't Elvia have her job interview today?
    B: _____. Her interview is tomorrow.
    A. No, she won't
    B. Yes, she did
    C. No, she didn't

20. **A:** _____ get eight paid sick days?
    B: Yes, they do. All employees get eight paid sick days per year.

    A. Haven't full-time employees
    B. Full-time employees aren't
    C. Don't full-time employees

21. **A:** _____ changed the schedule yet?
    B: No, but I think they're going to change it starting next week.

    A. Haven't they
    B. They don't
    C. They have

22. **A:** _____ talk to your supervisor?
    B: Yes. I explained the problem, but it's going to take time to work out a solution.

    A. You do
    B. Didn't you
    C. Have you

23. **A:** How was your performance review?
    B: OK. My boss said _____ to my production. Sometimes I don't work fast enough.

    A. to pay attention
    B. paying attention
    C. pays attention

24. **A:** The manager warned _____ our phone calls during work hours.
    B: So you can't make any personal calls from work?

    A. our limit
    B. we have to limit
    C. us to limit

25. **A:** I asked my coworker _____ her things on the desk when she's finished working.
    B: Good. I hope it helps.

    A. she doesn't leave
    B. don't leave
    C. not to leave

26. **A:** Did you read the memo in the break room?
    B: Yeah. They're advising workers _____ for employee benefits this week. Friday is the last day to enroll for benefits.

    A. to sign up
    B. signing up
    C. sign up

27. **A:** The boss reminded everyone _____ sandals on the job.
    B: Well, I guess that's a good rule. It's easy to get hurt with all the construction.

    A. don't wear
    B. not to wear
    C. not wear

READING I

Read. What is the correct answer: A, B, C, or D?

Three months ago, Heng started working at Butterchurn Farms. He's learning to communicate effectively with his supervisor and his coworkers. He double-checks if he's not sure about something. He asks questions to make sure he understands.

This month Heng had his first performance review. Mr. Klein, Heng's boss, gave him some feedback on his work. He told Heng some of the things he was doing well and some areas in which he needed to improve.

In general Mr. Klein is happy with Heng's work. Mr. Klein told Heng that he was meeting his quotas. He said Heng was good at working as part of a team and following instructions. He also expressed his concern that sometimes Heng didn't follow safety procedures. He reminded Heng to wear his safety gear at all times.

28. Mr. Klein gave Heng feedback. What does this mean?

    A. He invited Heng to eat lunch with him.

    B. He fixed the things Heng had done wrong.

    C. He said which things Heng was and wasn't doing well.

    D. He asked Heng questions.

29. In what way does Heng need to improve?

    A. He needs to give Mr. Klein a performance review.

    B. He needs to start meeting his quotas.

    C. He needs to start a new team to work with.

    D. He needs to wear his safety gear at all times.

READING II
Read. What is the correct answer: A, B, C, or D?

Prevent Repetitive Stress Injuries at Home

Many employers are now taking steps to help workers avoid repetitive stress injuries (RSIs). But you can be at risk for an RSI at home, too. Whether you're sending e-mails or using the Internet, if you spend too many hours on your home computer, you could develop RSIs such as carpal tunnel syndrome and tendonitis.

The good news is that you can control these RSIs in your home. Here are a few suggestions: Always sit up straight with your feet on the floor. Make sure you're not sitting too high or too low.

You can get an adjustable ergonomic chair, or you can add or take away cushions to adjust a chair you have. You might consider getting an ergonomic keyboard to protect your wrists. Also, take breaks. Stand up, stretch, walk around, and look away from the computer for a few minutes every hour to rest your back, neck, wrists, and eyes. Visit our website for more information about RSIs and how to prevent them at www.localweeklyjournal.com/RSI.

30. What is the main idea of this article?

A. RSIs can develop from sending e-mails and using the Internet.

B. Anyone who uses a computer is at risk for developing an RSI.

C. People can take steps to prevent RSIs at home.

D. It's important to take breaks from the computer to avoid RSIs.

31. Which of the following does the author recommend?

A. talking to your employer about how to avoid RSIs

B. working fewer hours

C. avoiding sending e-mails and using the Internet

D. regularly resting your eyes when you use a computer

WRITING

Read. What is the correct answer: A, B, C, or D?

McLeary Manufacturing

❶ To:

From:

Date:

❷ Re:

I'm writing to offer some solutions to the problem of employees beginning their shifts late.

In my last performance review, you pointed out that I sometimes started my shift late. I think some other employees are having the same problem for these reasons:

- The company parking lot is often full when we arrive. (Many passengers on the nearby commuter train park in our lot).

- It is very difficult to find other parking. Sometimes we have to drive very far to find another place to park.

❸ •

We can take these steps to discourage other people from parking in our lot.

- Put a sign at the entrance to the parking lot. The sign should explain that the lot is for McLeary employees only and that cars not belonging to McLeary workers will be towed.

- Give employees identification tags to hang on the rearview mirror of their cars when they're parked in the lot. The security guards can check that all the cars in the lot have tags. They can have any cars without tags towed away.

❹ •

We can help employees start their shifts on time by making sure that they can easily find parking in the company lot.

---

32. Where should the writer type the subject line?

A. 1

B. 2

C. 3

D. 4

33. Which of the following is the best subject line for this memo?

A. new sign

B. performance review

C. reasons why employees are late

D. ideas for improving employees' start times

Unit 5 Test

🔘 LISTENING I

(Tracks 36–37) You will hear a question. Then you will hear a conversation. After that, you will hear the question again and three choices. What is the correct answer: A, B, or C?

1. A. He suggests one way to prevent fires.
   B. He says what to do if there's a fire.
   C. He explains how to escape from a fire.

2. A. a natural disaster
   B. a weather report
   C. dangerous weather

🔘 LISTENING II

(Tracks 38–39) You will hear the first part of a conversation. To finish the conversation, listen and choose the correct answer: A, B, or C.

3. A. I'm at work.
   B. There's an emergency.
   C. My house is on fire.

4. A. You should try to prevent fires in your home.
   B. You should call 911.
   C. Many fires start in the kitchen.

🔘 LISTENING III

(Tracks 40–43) You will hear a conversation. Then you will hear three sentences. Which sentence is true: A, B, or C?

5. A. The roads might be dangerous.
   B. The woman is driving in the rain.
   C. The man isn't going to drive.

6. A. This is an emergency.
   B. The woman should evacuate.
   C. A man is bleeding.

7. A. Someone is going to call 911.
   B. The man is going to evacuate.
   C. There is a fire in the man's house.

8. A. There's a hurricane in the area now.
   B. There might be a hurricane in the area in the next few days.
   C. The woman watched the hurricane.

LIFE SKILLS

Look at the map on the next page and answer these questions. What is the correct answer: A, B, C, or D?

9. You're at ①. A major hurricane is coming from the Gulf of Mexico, and you need to evacuate. Which route do you need to take in order to evacuate?

   A. go north on CORD 767

   B. go south on CORD 767

   C. go east on STHY 78

   D. go west on STHY 78

10. You're at ②. Which direction do you need to go in order to evacuate?

    A. north, then east

    B. east, then north

    C. south, then west

    D. west, then north

11. You're at ③. Which direction should you go in order to evacuate?

    A. northeast

    B. northwest

    C. west

    D. southeast

12. You're at ④. Which two routes can you take from here to evacuate?

    A. STHY 867 and CORD 767

    B. CORD 869 and USHY 4

    C. San Carlos Blvd. and USHY 41

    D. STHY 867 and CORD 869

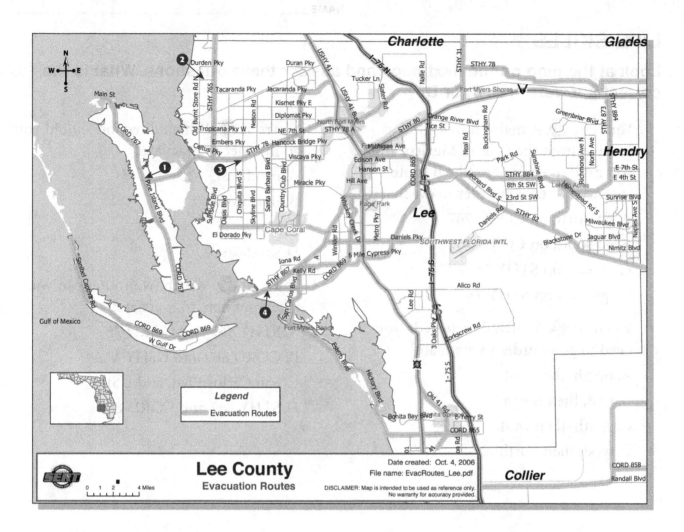

Lee County
Evacuation Routes

Legend
Evacuation Routes

Date created: Oct. 4, 2006
File name: EvacRoutes_Lee.pdf

DISCLAIMER: Map is intended to be used as reference only.
No warranty for accuracy provided.

0 1 2   4 Miles

GRAMMAR

Complete each conversation. What is the correct answer: A, B, or C?

13. **A:** How can I make my home safer?
    B: If you _____ you need to get some.

    A. don't have smoke detectors,
    B. have smoke detectors,
    C. will have smoke detectors,

14. **A:** What can I do to prepare for an emergency?
    B: If you _____ an emergency plan, you should definitely make one.

    A. can't have
    B. not have
    C. don't have

15. **A:** What should I do if my clothes catch on fire?
    B: _____ if your clothes are on fire.

    A. You should roll on the ground
    B. You might roll on the ground
    C. When you roll on the ground

16. **A:** If _____ to keep a space heater on while you sleep?
    B: No. You should never leave a space heater on while you sleep.

    A. it's very cold, it's OK
    B. it's very cold, is it OK
    C. is it very cold, is it OK

17. **A:** What is the first thing _____ a fire in your house?
    B: The first thing you should do is leave the house.

    A. you should do, if there's
    B. you should do if, there's
    C. you should do if there's

18. **A:** How can I stay safe during an earthquake?
    B: _____ you feel the earth shake, get under a piece of furniture.

    A. Before
    B. As soon as
    C. Until

19. **A:** I'm going to make a fire escape plan.
    B: That's great. _____ the plan, you should practice it with your family.

    A. You might make
    B. After you make
    C. You must make

20. **A:** What's a hurricane warning?

  B: The National Weather Service issues a hurricane warning _____ a hurricane to arrive in your area within twenty-four hours.

  A. when you can expect

  B. until you expect

  C. you must expect

21. **A:** Did you lose power during the thunderstorm?

  B: Yes, but we were prepared. _____ we put new batteries in our flashlights.

  A. After the storm started,

  B. Before the storm started,

  C. If the storm starts,

22. **A:** I really want to leave, but I don't like to drive in the rain. And it's raining really hard!

  B: I know. I want to go, too, but we should wait _____ it stops raining.

  A. when

  B. after

  C. until

23. **A:** What's wrong with Stanley?

  B: He _____ an allergic reaction, but we're not sure.

  A. might be having

  B. must be having

  C. can't be having

24. **A:** There's an ambulance in front of our apartment building.

  B: Oh no. There _____ a medical emergency.

  A. must be

  B. couldn't be

  C. might not be

25. **A:** I've been really tired lately, and I don't know why.

  B: _____ sick?

  A. May be getting

  B. If you're getting

  C. Could you be getting

26. **A:** Did the baby fall down?

  B: Yes, but she's not crying, so it _____ very much. I think she's fine.

  A. could hurt

  B. may be

  C. must not hurt

27. **A:** This smoke alarm doesn't work. Maybe we need to change the batteries.

  B: No, I put new batteries in it yesterday, so that _____ the problem.

  A. can't be

  B. must be

  C. could be

READING I

Read. What is the correct answer: A, B, C, or D?

The Most Important Call You'll Ever Make
Knowing how to use 911 could save someone's life.

911 is an emergency response system in the United States.
Dial 911 any time there is a medical emergency, a fire emergency,
or a police emergency. This call is free from any phone.

Stay calm
When you call 911, stay calm. The 911 operator will ask you questions
and then send help—an ambulance, the fire department, or police officers.

Give answers
Be prepared to give the following information:
- the type of emergency (Say what the emergency is.)
- the location of the emergency (Give the address and the
  cross streets or the closest intersection.)
- details about the emergency (Say what happened, what's
  being done, etc.)
- your name and the phone number you're calling from

Don't hang up
Do not hang up until help arrives. Stay on the phone because the 911 operator
might have more questions or more instructions for you.

28. What is the main idea of this article?

A. Emergencies can happen to anyone.

B. It's important to know how to use 911.

C. There are many different kinds of
emergencies.

D. Answer the 911 operator's questions
quickly.

29. What is the author's purpose in this article?

A. to entertain

B. to persuade

C. to give an opinion

D. to inform

READING II

Rodrigo Tapia and his wife, Isabel, live in San Diego, California, where there are sometimes earthquakes. The Tapias have an emergency plan, and they know what to do during an earthquake. They also know that life after an earthquake can be difficult, so it's important to be prepared. Sometimes the water isn't safe to drink or there's no water. Often there's no electricity. If this happens, Rodrigo and Isabel want to be ready. So they keep emergency supplies to use until life returns to normal. They have water and food. They also have a radio and batteries. They made a kit of first aid supplies in case there's a medical emergency.

Rodrigo and Isabel hope they never need to use their emergency supplies. But if they do, they'll be ready.

30. Why do Rodrigo and Isabel have emergency supplies?

    A. They are required by law to have emergency supplies.

    B. There was an earthquake, but Rodrigo and Isabel weren't ready.

    C. They want to be ready for life after an earthquake.

    D. They hope they don't have to use the emergency supplies.

31. Which is true?

    A. Rodrigo and Isabel would prefer not to use their emergency supplies.

    B. Rodrigo and Isabel need to find out what to do during an earthquake.

    C. Rodrigo and Isabel don't have supplies for a medical emergency.

    D. Rodrigo and Isabel need to make an emergency plan.

WRITING

Read. What is the correct answer: A, B, C, or D?

Steps to Take Before and After a Hurricane

I've never lived through a hurricane. But I just moved to Florida, and I know that I need to be prepared in case there is one. So I talked to my neighbors to learn what I need to do.

32. Which of the following sentences should the writer use to begin explaining the steps?

A. When the government says to evacuate, I'll get my supplies, and I'll leave.

B. Before hurricane season begins, I need to buy some supplies, such as bottled water, nonperishable food, a first aid kit, flashlights, and a radio.

C. After the storm, I need to listen to the news. I have to wait until the local government says I can go home.

D. When I get home again, I need to check my house carefully. There may be dangers such as fallen electrical wires.

33. Which of the following should the writer end the paragraph with?

A. Then I need to plan my evacuation route.

B. When there is a hurricane watch, I need to listen to the weather reports and the local government's instructions about evacuating.

C. After the storm, I need to listen to the news. I have to wait until the local government says I can go home.

D. Finally, I'll work with my neighbors. We can help one another until life returns to normal.

Unit 6 Test

🔊 LISTENING I

(Tracks 44–46) You will hear a question. Then you will hear a conversation. After that, you will hear the question again and three choices. What is the correct answer: A, B, or C?

1. A. park on the street
    B. park in the lot behind the building
    C. put a permit on the mirror

2. A. go to the apartment now
    B. call someone
    C. go to the apartment in an hour

3. A. The neighbors' TV is loud.
    B. The woman can't hear her music.
    C. The neighbors are playing loud music.

🔊 LISTENING II

(Tracks 47–48) You will hear the first part of a conversation. To finish the conversation, listen and choose the correct answer: A, B, or C.

4. A. No, we didn't. It's in good condition.
    B. We have to pay for damage to the apartment.
    C. The security deposit is one month's rent.

5. A. It starts on September 1.
    B. It's for a year.
    C. It's $1,000 a month.

🔊 LISTENING III

(Tracks 49–51) You will hear a conversation. Then you will hear three sentences. Which sentence is true: A, B, or C?

6. A. The landlord pays for gas.
    B. The cost is $1,100 a month plus water.
    C. The cost is $1,100 a month plus gas and electric.

7. A. The landlord can't raise the rent now.
    B. The lease started on March 31.
    C. The rent now is $900 a month.

8. A. The woman talked to her neighbors.
    B. The woman called the building manager.
    C. The woman smokes in her apartment.

LIFE SKILLS

Read the next page and answer these questions. What is the correct answer: A, B, C, or D?

9. How much did the tenant give the landlord for a security deposit?

   A. $1,125

   B. $1,125 each month

   C. $25

   D. $1,000

10. Which utilities does the tenant have to pay for?

    A. heat and hot water only

    B. all utilities

    C. all utilities except heat and hot water

    D. heat, hot water, and electricity

11. Which of the following is the landlord's responsibility?

    A. delivering rent on the first day of each month

    B. putting a smoke detector in each apartment

    C. cleaning inside and outside each apartment

    D. using garbage and recyclable containers

12. Which of the following is the tenant's responsibility?

    A. returning the security deposit at the end of the rental agreement

    B. keeping the security deposit

    C. repairing appliances in the apartment if they break

    D. paying rent by or before the first day of each month

Lease Agreement

PARTIES: The parties to this agreement are
___Celia Reyes___ , herein referred to as LANDLORD, and
___Keerat Gupta___ , herein referred to as TENANT.

TERM: This agreement is to begin on ___January 1, 2010___
and is an agreement for the term of ___12 months___ ,
ending on _December 31, 2010_.

RENT: Rent is ___$1,225___ per month, payment due on
the _1st_ day of each month, and will be delivered to
___Celia Reyes, 1821 Regal Ave., Tempe, AZ 85384___ .
A late fee of ___$25___ will be added for rent that is paid
after the _5th_ day of the month.

SECURITY DEPOSIT: Tenant has paid to landlord and
landlord acknowledges receipt of ___$1,000___ as a
cleaning and security deposit. Landlord may keep all or
any part of this deposit upon termination of this rental
agreement for any of the following reasons:
- to cover unpaid rent owed to landlord
- to pay the cost of repairing any damage to the
  premises resulting from abuse, misuse, or neglect,
  not including normal wear and tear

UTILITIES: Tenant agrees to pay for all utilities except
___heat and hot water___ , which shall be paid by landlord.

LANDLORD SHALL:
- provide a CO detector and a smoke alarm in
  each apartment
- keep the appliances in the apartment in good
  working order
- keep the public areas of the building in a clean
  and safe condition

TENANT SHALL:
- pay rent on or before due date
- keep the apartment in a clean and safe condition
- place garbage and recyclable items in the
  containers provided

TENANT SHALL NOT:
- make changes to the premises without
  permission of landlord
- smoke on the premises
- keep a pet on the premises

GRAMMAR

Complete each conversation. What is the correct answer: A, B, or C?

13. **A:** _____ smoke in their apartments?
    B: No. There is no smoking anywhere in the building.

    A. Are tenants allowed to
    B. Tenants aren't required to
    C. Tenants are supposed to

14. **A:** Could you leave the front door of the building unlocked for me?
    B: Sorry, I can't. We _____ keep the door locked.

    A. aren't supposed to
    B. are supposed to
    C. aren't required to

15. **A:** Do you have a cat?
    B: No. I live in an apartment, and we're _____ have pets.

    A. required to
    B. not permitted to
    C. supposed to

16. **A:** Does the apartment have a washer and dryer?
    B: No, it doesn't. But there's a laundry room. Tenants _____ use it from 6:00 A.M. to 11:00 P.M.

    A. aren't supposed to
    B. are required to
    C. are allowed to

17. **A:** We _____ separate recyclable materials from garbage.
    B: OK. Which container is for recyclable things and which is for garbage?

    A. 're allowed to
    B. 're not permitted to
    C. 're supposed to

18. **A:** Tenants don't pay for electricity, _____?
    B: No. The landlord pays for all utilities.

    A. do they
    B. don't they
    C. they don't

19. **A:** The lease started in November, _____?
    B: Yes, it started on November 1.

    A. didn't they
    B. doesn't it
    C. didn't it

20. A: The landlord isn't going to return my security deposit.
   B: Why? The apartment isn't damaged, _____?
   A. is it
   B. isn't it
   C. doesn't it

21. A: Mina doesn't have any pets, _____?
   B: No. She wants to get a dog, but her apartment is too small.
   A. doesn't she
   B. does she
   C. has she

22. A: The landlord says we have to pay a $25 late fee. But the rent wasn't late, _____?
   B: No. Actually, I paid it early. I'll call him tomorrow.
   A. wasn't it
   B. it wasn't
   C. was it

23. A: Did you talk to the landlord yet about the leaking ceiling?
   B: Yes. He said _____ to look at it today around noon. Will you be home then?
   A. he comes
   B. he would come
   C. he came

24. A: That car is always parked in front of the mailbox. Whose car is it?
   B: Megan said _____ to the guy in 3A.
   A. it would belong
   B. it belonged
   C. did it belong

25. A: Is the window in your apartment fixed yet?
   B: No, but my roommate said the building manager _____ it tomorrow.
   A. has fixed
   B. fixes
   C. would fix

26. A: How did you find out about the neighbors' new dog?
   B: I saw them in the elevator yesterday. _____ me that they just got a puppy.
   A. They told
   B. They said
   C. They would tell

27. A: Did anyone tell the building manager about the broken lock on the front door?
   B: Yes. Kavita just called him, and she told him that the door _____ properly.
   A. not closed
   B. not close
   C. doesn't close

READING I

Read. What is the correct answer: A, B, C, or D?

Sacha and Livia are friends and roommates. They recently signed a twelve-month lease on an apartment. By signing the lease, Sacha and Livia agreed to pay $950 for rent on the first day of each month. Utilities are not included, so Sacha and Livia are also responsible for those. Sacha and Livia paid a security deposit of $1,000, which they'll get back at the end of the lease if they don't owe any rent and the apartment is in good condition.

When they signed the lease, Sacha and Livia agreed to some other rules, too. They can't smoke in the apartment or have any pets. They can't change anything in the house without the landlord's permission. Finally, they agreed not to play music or the TV loudly.

28. Who pays for electricity?

    A. Sacha and Livia pay for it.

    B. The landlord pays for all utilities, including electricity.

    C. The landlord pays for it if the apartment is in good condition.

    D. Electricity is included in the cost of the rent.

29. What two things must Sacha and Livia do to get back their security deposit at the end of the lease?

    A. agree to the rules and get the landlord's permission to change anything

    B. pay all the rent and keep the apartment in good condition

    C. not smoke and not have pets in the apartment

    D. keep the apartment in good condition and play their music and TV quietly

READING II
Read. What is the correct answer: A, B, C, or D?

Before You Sign ...

So you've found a great place to rent. Now it's time to sign the lease and move in, right? Not so fast. Here are a few tips that will help protect you before you sign a lease.

Talk to other tenants in the building. Ask how they like living there. Ask if there are any concerns with living in the building that you might not notice during a visit. Try to have this conversation when the landlord isn't there—it's more likely you'll get honest answers.

If you decide to sign the lease, visit the apartment again. This time look closely for any problems. Check all the appliances and electrical outlets to be sure they work. Turn on all the faucets to be sure there is hot water. Flush the toilets. Look for any broken windows, cracks in the walls, or stains on the walls or carpets. Make a list of any problems you find, and have the landlord sign and date the list. Discuss with the landlord any problems that need to be fixed before you move in. Then make a final list of anything that won't be fixed. Have the landlord sign and date this. Do this before you sign the lease so that you're not responsible for any damage that was done before you moved in.

---

30. Which of the following is the main idea of this article?

　A. It's important to talk to the neighbors before you sign a lease.

　B. Landlords can cause problems for tenants.

　C. Talking to other tenants can help you avoid landlord problems in the future.

　D. Tenants can protect themselves by taking a few steps before signing a rental lease.

31. Which of the following details support(s) the main idea?

　A. You should look for any problems in the apartment you're considering renting.

　B. You should sign the lease as soon as you find an apartment you like.

　C. You should talk to people who already live in the building where you're considering living.

　D. Both A and C are correct.

WRITING

Read. What is the correct answer: A, B, C, or D?

Femi Mubarak rents an apartment from Gregory James. Femi has a big problem. For the past two days, her refrigerator has been leaking water, and it's not keeping the food cold. She's called Mr. James several times and left him messages, but he hasn't called her back. So she's decided to e-mail him. She wants the refrigerator fixed or replaced today. She wants Mr. James to call her so they can set up a time for someone to go to the apartment.

○○○

From: Femi Mubarak (f.mubarak@yazzmail.com)
Subject: refrigerator not working
Date: December 12, 2009
To: Gregory James (greg_james@gregjames.com)

Dear Mr. James,
I'm a tenant in apartment 3C. For the past two days, I haven't been able to reach you by phone. I've left you several messages, but you haven't returned my calls.

_____
(32.)
The refrigerator needs to be fixed or replaced immediately. According to my lease, the landlord is responsible for fixing any problems with appliances.

_____
(33.)
I look forward to hearing from you very soon.

Sincerely,
Femi Mubarak

32. Which of the following sentences should the writer use to clearly state her problem?

A. I'm writing because you haven't called me back. A landlord is supposed to be available to help tenants with problems.

B. I'm writing because I need someone to look at the refrigerator. You need to look at it today.

C. I'm writing to let you know that my refrigerator is broken. It is leaking water, and it's not keeping the food cold.

D. I'm writing to tell you about a problem. It's a big problem, and I need help.

33. Which of the following sentences should the writer use to clearly ask for a solution to the problem?

A. Will you please send someone today to look at the refrigerator and fix or replace it? Please call me at 702-555-2839 to arrange a time.

B. Why haven't you called me? In the future, please call me back when I leave you messages. My number is 702-555-2839.

C. Why is the refrigerator having this problem? Before I moved in, you told me that the appliances were new.

D. How can we fix this problem? I'm very frustrated because the refrigerator hasn't worked for two days.

Unit 7 Test

LISTENING I

(Tracks 52–54) **You will hear a question. Then you will hear a conversation. After that, you will hear the question again and three choices. What is the correct answer: A, B, or C?**

1. A. power steering
    B. a sunroof
    C. air-conditioning

2. A. a dealer
    B. an individual
    C. a private owner

3. A. after a car accident
    B. each month
    C. each year

LISTENING II

(Tracks 55–56) **You will hear the first part of a conversation. To finish the conversation, listen and choose the correct answer: A, B, or C.**

4. A. 35,000 miles.
    B. 19 miles per gallon.
    C. Every 3,000 miles.

5. A. It's a 2009 SUV.
    B. Sure. I'll check them and let you know.
    C. Yes, you should use your windshield wipers in bad weather.

LISTENING III

(Tracks 57–59) **You will hear a conversation. Then you will hear three sentences. Which sentence is true: A, B, or C?**

6. A. The man prefers two-door cars.
    B. The man would rather have a red car than a blue car.
    C. The man would rather have a four-door car.

7. A. The officer filled out an accident report.
    B. The woman has to show her vehicle registration.
    C. The woman has to renew her insurance.

8. A. The woman didn't use her turn signal.
    B. The woman was moving into the left lane.
    C. The other driver started to slow down before he saw the woman's car.

LIFE SKILLS I

Read. What is the correct answer: A, B, C, or D?

Drive Smart Auto Insurance   1-888-555-1919   www.drivesmartautoinsurance.com

NEW JERSEY STATE INSURANCE IDENTIFICATION CARD

Policy Number:	Effective Date:	Expiration Date:
0029-33-29-17	4/12/2010 (12:01 A.M.)	10/12/2010 (12:01 A.M.)

Applicable with respect to the following motor vehicle.

Vargas, Blanca	**Year**	**Make**	**Model**
254 Summer Ln.	2000	Acura	Integra LS
Hackensack, NJ 07601			

Name and Address of Issuer:
Drive Smart Auto Insurance
100 Insurance Rd.
Trenton, NJ 08608

Vehicle Identification Number:
2I3AS29T38294738

Company Code: 102

9. Which of the following is true?

A. Blanca's coverage begins at noon on April 12, 2010.

B. Blanca Vargas has car insurance for six months.

C. This card is good for one year.

D. Blanca's car was made in 2010.

LIFE SKILLS II

Read. What is the correct answer: A, B, C, or D?

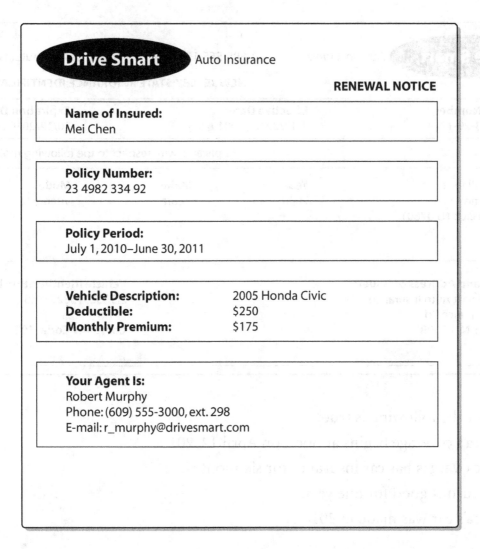

Drive Smart Auto Insurance

RENEWAL NOTICE

Name of Insured:
Mei Chen

Policy Number:
23 4982 334 92

Policy Period:
July 1, 2010–June 30, 2011

Vehicle Description: 2005 Honda Civic
Deductible: $250
Monthly Premium: $175

Your Agent Is:
Robert Murphy
Phone: (609) 555-3000, ext. 298
E-mail: r_murphy@drivesmart.com

10. Who is Mei Chen?

A. the person who sold the car

B. the owner of the car

C. an employee of Drive Smart Auto Insurance

D. the insurance agent

11. How much does this policy cost?

A. $250 a year

B. $250 a month

C. $175 a month

D. $175 a year

12. The owner of the car got into an accident. It will cost $1,000 to fix the damage to the car. Which sentence is true?

A. The insurance company will pay the full amount of the cost to fix the car.

B. The owner won't pay anything if the accident happened between July 1, 2010 and June 30, 2011.

C. The owner has to pay $175 and the insurance company will pay the rest.

D. The owner and the insurance company will each pay part of the repair costs.

GRAMMAR

Complete each conversation. What is the correct answer: A, B, or C?

13. **A:** You should think about getting an SUV. They're great.

    B: I know they're popular, but I'd rather _____ that doesn't use a lot of gas.

    A. to get something
    B. getting something
    C. get something

14. **A:** Would she prefer a compact car _____ a full-size car?

    B: No, she wouldn't. She doesn't like small cars.

    A. to
    B. than
    C. that

15. **A:** _____ to drive a light-colored car or a dark one?

    B: It doesn't really matter to me.

    A. Would you rather
    B. Would you prefer
    C. Would you prefer a

16. **A:** Do you want to drive downtown, or do you want to take the bus?

    B: I'd _____ drive. It's always so hard to find a place to park.

    A. prefer
    B. rather not
    C. prefer not

17. **A:** Which model do you like better—the two-door or the four-door?

    B: Well, I'd _____ to have a four-door car. What about you?

    A. prefer
    B. rather
    C. rather not

18. **A:** My car has been making a strange noise lately.

    B: Hmm. I wonder _____. I can take a look at it if you want.

    A. what problem
    B. what is the problem
    C. what the problem is

19. **A:** I don't know _____ a new car or a used one.

    B: Well, that depends on several things. There are advantages and disadvantages to both.

    A. should I buy
    B. whether I should buy
    C. do I buy

20. **A:** Excuse me. Can you tell me _____?
    B: Sure. They're $16.99 each.

    A. how much are these windshield wipers

    B. how are these windshield wipers

    C. how much these windshield wipers are

21. **A:** My car needs new tires. Do you know _____ at Reynold's Auto Parts?
    B: Yes, I think they have them there.

    A. they sell them

    B. whether they sell them

    C. do they sell them

22. **A:** I want to know _____ pick up my car.
    B: It'll be ready today at 4:00.

    A. what time can I

    B. what time I can

    C. when can I

23. **A:** Had Luisa _____ the other driver before she called the police?
    B: No, the first thing she did after the accident was call the police.

    A. talked to

    B. talk to

    C. talking to

24. **A:** I heard that Charlie bought a new car. What kind did he get?
    B: Well, _____ to get a minivan, but in the end he chose an SUV.

    A. he had planned

    B. he has planned

    C. he would rather

25. **A:** I really like your new car. How did you decide what kind to get?
    B: Well, I _____ a lot of research online before I even looked at any cars. So I had a good idea of what I wanted.

    A. have done

    B. had done

    C. has done

26. **A:** I heard you had a car accident this morning. What happened?
    B: I had just _____ onto the highway, when a car ran into me. Luckily, there wasn't too much damage.

    A. get

    B. got

    C. gotten

27. **A:** Had they saved a lot of money before they bought their car?
    B: No, they _____. That's why they bought a used car instead of a new one.

    A. hadn't saved

    B. hadn't

    C. haven't

READING I

Read. What is the correct answer: A, B, C, or D?

Nami's car was making a strange noise, so she took it to her friend Hiroshi, who is a mechanic. Hiroshi fixed the problem, and he checked the rest of the car, too. Hiroshi said the car was in good condition, and he gave Nami some advice on car maintenance.

He said Nami needs to check the oil regularly. She should change it when it's black. She should also check other fluids, such as the engine coolant, transmission fluid, and brake fluid about every two weeks. She needs to add more fluids when they're low. Hiroshi also warned Nami not to forget about the tires. He said to check the air pressure when she gets gas, or about once a week. And he recommended checking the tires' treads regularly, about once a month, to make sure they're not too worn.

28. According to Hiroshi, what should Nami do every two weeks?

A. change the oil

B. check the tires' treads

C. add more fluids

D. check the engine coolant

29. According to Hiroshi, how often should Nami check the air pressure of the tires?

A. once a week

B. every two weeks

C. once a month

D. every other month

READING II

Read. What is the correct answer: A, B, C, or D?

THE DAILY COMMUTE

Millions of adults are employed in the United States. How do all those people commute, or get to work? In several different ways.

Many people choose to drive to work alone. One advantage of driving alone is that you don't have to rely on any schedule but your own. But, some people have found alternative ways to commute. Some people carpool, or drive to work together. They share the costs of driving, and they have people to talk to. Public transportation, such as buses, trains, and subways, are an option for some people. This is often an inexpensive way to commute. Other people live close enough to work that they can walk there. That can be a great way to get some exercise. And some people find other ways to get to work, for example, by riding motorcycles or bicycles to their jobs. Lastly, some people don't commute at all—people who work from home don't need to go anywhere to get to their jobs.

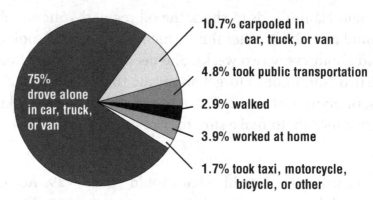

Percentages of total workers in the United States 2006

75% drove alone in car, truck, or van

10.7% carpooled in car, truck, or van

4.8% took public transportation

2.9% walked

3.9% worked at home

1.7% took taxi, motorcycle, bicycle, or other

Source: Research and Innovative Technology Administration, Bureau of Transportation Statistics

30. What's the purpose of this article?

A. to show that more people are working from home than ever before

B. to explain why people should consider different ways of getting to work

C. to convince people to carpool or take public transportation instead of driving alone

D. to provide information about how people in the United States get to work

31. Look at the pie chart. How did most Americans get to work in 2006?

A. They drove alone.

B. They drove in a carpool.

C. They took public transportation.

D. They walked.

WRITING

Read. What is the correct answer: A, B, C, or D?

Smart Shopper

I'm a smart shopper. I like to get good deals, and for me, that means getting what I want at a good price. I do research before I buy things, especially before I make any big purchases. Last year I used my research skills to get a good deal on a used car. Safety was very important to me. So I began by doing some research to find out which cars have the best safety features. _____ I (32.) learned about the average repair costs of those cars. I found out about their gas mileage, too. Next, I looked at newspaper ads and at some different websites to compare prices of different models. Then it was time to start test-driving cars. I went to several dealerships in my area. A few days later, I found a car that was perfect for me—but I didn't buy it that day. I took the car to a mechanic and asked him to check it out. He said everything looked OK. And after all that, I did it. _____, I bought a (33.) car! My car was a good deal. It wasn't cheap, but it has the features I want, and I paid a good price for what I got.

---

32. Which word could introduce this sentence by correctly signaling when the action occurred in the paragraph above?

_____, I learned about the average repair costs of those cars.

A. First

B. Then

C. Finally

D. Before

33. Which word could introduce this sentence by correctly signaling when the action occurred in the paragraph above?

_____, I bought a car!

A. Next

B. On the first day

C. And

D. Finally

Unit 8 Test

💿 LISTENING I

(Tracks 60–61) You will hear a question. Then you will hear a conversation. After that, you will hear the question again and three choices. What is the correct answer: A, B, or C?

1. A. The man should start making healthy meals.
    B. The man should get more exercise.
    C. The kids should eat breakfast every day.

2. A. answer the patient's questions
    B. give the patient medicine
    C. examine the patient

💿 LISTENING II

(Tracks 62–64) You will hear the first part of a conversation. To finish conversation, listen and choose the correct answer: A, B, or C.

3. A. I'd like to make an appointment.
    B. I've been sneezing and coughing a lot lately.
    C. The symptoms began two days ago.

4. A. She can't speak.
    B. No, she isn't in pain.
    C. Yes, she is.

5. A. I've been feeling dizzy, and I've been getting headaches.
    B. I've been taking my medicine regularly.
    C. I've been here for about fifteen minutes.

💿 LISTENING III

(Tracks 65–67) You will hear a conversation. Then you will hear three sentences. Which sentence is true: A, B, or C?

6. A. Anyone can get a checkup at the health fair.
    B. Immunizations will be available for $10.
    C. Checkups are going to be free for children.

7. A. The man should take the medicine once a day.
    B. The medication doesn't have any side effects.
    C. The man should take the medicine when he feels sleepy.

8. A. This is a medical emergency.
    B. The woman wants to improve her health.
    C. The man is overweight.

LIFE SKILLS

Read the next page and answer these questions. What is the correct answer: A, B, C, or D?

9. What is the last day that Chao can enroll in the company's health insurance plan?

    A. January 14, 2010

    B. February 2, 2010

    C. March 2, 2010

    D. October 1, 2010

10. What does Chao want to do at this time?

    A. use his wife's health insurance plan

    B. officially join the company's health insurance plan

    C. make a change to his current health insurance plan

    D. choose not to join his company's health insurance plan

11. Who besides himself does Chao want to be covered?

    A. his wife only

    B. his daughter only

    C. his two daughters

    D. his wife and his daughter

12. Which of the following sentences describes Chao's situation?

    A. Chao's employment status will change this year.

    B. Chao will need to make changes to his health insurance plan soon.

    C. Chao is a new employee of the company.

    D. Chao is a part-time employee.

Scott Pro Shipping Company
Health Insurance Enrollment and Changes Form

Open Enrollment Period
Employees wishing to participate in the company's health insurance plan must enroll within one month of date of hire. Changes can be made only during the last two weeks of January or the first two weeks of October.

SECTION 1: Complete the following personal information.
Name: (first) _Chao_   (last) _Tang_
Street Address: _352 Polk Ave._
City, State, Zip: _Salem, OR 97304_
Phone: _503-555-7091_
Starting Date: _2/2/10_
Social Security Number: _987-54-3210_
☑ Male   ☐ Female
Birth date: _12/12/79_
Marital Status: ☐ Single   ☑ Married
Employment Status: ☑ Full-Time   ☐ Part-Time

SECTION 2: Select (✓) one type of enrollment.
☑ Enroll
☐ Change (I would like a different type of plan.)
☐ Waive (I do not wish to enroll in the company plan at this time.)

SECTION 3: Indicate which family members you wish to cover.
☑ Self   ☑ Spouse   ☑ Dependents

Name (first, last) of all family members to be covered.	Birth date
Spouse: _Liu Tang_	_04/07/81_
Dependent: _Jia Tang_	_06/17/05_
Dependent: _____	_____
Dependent: _____	_____

SECTION 4: Indicate reasons(s) for completing this form.
☑ New Employee
☐ Change of plan because of:
          ☐ Marriage   ☐ Divorce   ☐ Birth   ☐ Spouse's Employment

GRAMMAR

Complete each conversation. What is the correct answer: A, B, or C?

13. **A:** I heard you were sick last week. Are you feeling better?

    B: Yes, thanks. I _____ plenty of rest, and that has helped a lot.

    A. was getting
    B. 've been getting
    C. 's gotten

14. **A:** How long _____ this way?

    B: About two weeks. And the symptoms have gotten worse this week.

    A. have you been feeling
    B. you've been feeling
    C. are you feeling

15. **A:** So, what seems to be the matter?

    B: Well, sometimes my feet get numb. It's been going on _____ about a month.

    A. since
    B. for
    C. by

16. **A:** Things at work have been really crazy, and it's affecting me even outside of work. I _____ eating, and I can't sleep well, either.

    B: It sounds like you're really stressed.

    A. not been
    B. have not
    C. haven't been

17. **A:** You look good. Are you doing anything differently?

    B: Yes. I _____ making time each day to do something for myself—like taking a bath or reading. I feel wonderful!

    A. have been
    B. have
    C. had better

18. **A:** My schedule is _____ full that I don't have time to exercise.

    B: Well, you can start by making small changes in your routine, like taking the stairs at work instead of the elevator.

    A. such
    B. so
    C. so much

19. **A:** How was your doctor's appointment?

    B: It was fine, once I actually saw the doctor. But she had _____ patients that I had to wait for two hours.

    A. so many
    B. so much
    C. such

20. **A:** Have you lost weight? You look wonderful.

   B: Thanks. I'm exercising, and I'm watching what I eat. It has made _____ a change in how I feel that I can't believe it.

   A. so much
   B. so
   C. such

21. **A:** There's _____ information about different diets that it's hard to know which one is the best.

   B: Well, the most important thing is to eat a balanced diet that includes lots of fruits and vegetables and whole grains.

   A. so
   B. such
   C. so much

22. **A:** Exercise is _____ important to maintaining good health that some health insurance plans pay part of the cost of a gym membership.

   B: Really? I should check to see if my health insurance plan does that.

   A. so
   B. so much
   C. so many

23. **A:** I need to make some changes to my health insurance plan.

   B: You'd _____ do it soon. Friday is the last day to make changes.

   A. better
   B. ought to
   C. should

24. **A:** The label on the bottle says to take two pills. But my headache is really bad, so I'm going to take three.

   B: No, that could be dangerous. You _____ not take more than what the label says.

   A. ought to
   B. had better
   C. shouldn't

25. **A:** My mom got a cut on her hand, and it's taking a long time to heal. I wonder if something is wrong.

   B: She _____ to make an appointment for a doctor to look at it. That way you'll know for sure.

   A. had better
   B. ought
   C. should

26. **A:** Did you know that you can get a flu shot for free at the community health clinic?

   B: No, I didn't. I _____ take my dad. The doctor said it's a good idea for him to get a flu shot every year.

   A. ought
   B. better
   C. should

27. **A:** All students _____ receive immunizations before they start classes. They can't go to school without them.

   B: Our kids have already had their immunizations. I'll send the records tomorrow.

   A. had better
   B. should
   C. must

READING I

Read. What is the correct answer: A, B, C, or D?

Help yourself stay healthy!

Eat well. A healthy diet will help you control your weight, and it can prevent or control many conditions and diseases. Start each day with a good breakfast.

Drink water. Healthy adults need at least eight to ten 8-ounce glasses of water each day.

Exercise. Exercise is necessary for good health. It can help reduce stress, control weight, and keep your blood pressure at a healthy level. Choose activities that you enjoy, and make them part of your life.

Reduce stress. Stress can create problems in our bodies. It's important to find ways to reduce stress. One way is to get regular exercise. Also, it's very important to make time to relax and to do activities you enjoy.

Get enough sleep. Most people need seven to nine hours of sleep a night. Many people don't get enough sleep, and if this continues over time, it can lead to illness.

---

28. What is the main idea of this article?

A. Not getting enough sleep can lead to illness.

B. There are many things people can do to stay healthy.

C. Exercise is important for losing weight and reducing stress.

D. You should talk to your doctor to learn how you can stay healthy.

29. Which of the following does the article recommend?

A. drinking an 8-ounce glass of water before bed

B. checking your blood pressure every day

C. sleeping at least nine hours a night

D. making time to relax

READING II

Read. What is the correct answer: A, B, C, or D?

Marisol is very busy. She has two jobs, and she's taking some classes, too. A few weeks ago, Marisol started to feel sick. She felt weak, and she had aches and pains all over her body. So she decided to see a doctor.

Marisol told the doctor about her symptoms. The doctor asked Marisol some questions. He wanted to know about her work, how much sleep she was getting, and what she did for fun.

The doctor didn't give Marisol any medicine, but he gave her some instructions. He said that the stress in Marisol's life was making her sick. The doctor said Marisol needed to exercise more, relax, and make time for enjoyable activities. He said these things would help reduce Marisol's stress and make her feel better.

---

30. Why did Marisol go to the doctor?

    A. She was not feeling well.

    B. She thought she had allergies.

    C. She wanted to relax.

    D. She was so sick that she couldn't go to work.

31. What is one thing the doctor told Marisol to do?

    A. sleep more

    B. stop eating certain foods

    C. exercise

    D. take medicine

WRITING

Read. What is the correct answer: A, B, C, or D?

I was sitting in the dentist's chair, anxiously waiting for Gina, the hygienist, to start cleaning my teeth. My stomach was in knots. My sweaty hands held the chair tightly. Gina pushed a button, and the chair slowly reclined until I was nearly lying down. Then she temporarily blinded me as she pulled down a bright light and shined it right in my eyes.

Gina quickly adjusted the light. She asked me to open my mouth. First she used a metal instrument with a sharp point at one end to scrape tartar (hard yellow material) off my teeth. It didn't hurt, but it felt strange, and it sounded terrible. The horrible sound of metal on my teeth made me feel sick inside! Gina must have noticed that I was uncomfortable. She stopped for a moment. She told me to relax. I tried to focus on my breathing. That helped a little. After a few more minutes, she was finished. Whew! Relief washed over me.

Then Gina moved on. She picked up a metal tool with a little rubbery round thing on one end. The round thing spun around quickly and buzzed when Gina pushed a button. She put a little bit of toothpaste on the round thing, and she told me to open my mouth. _____
(33.)

32. Which of the following sentences from the story above uses sensory details?

A. My sweaty hands held the chair tightly.

B. Gina quickly adjusted the light.

C. She stopped for a moment.

D. After a few more minutes, she was finished.

33. Which of the following sentences would best complete the third paragraph using sensory details?

A. It was a whitening toothpaste, and it made my teeth very white.

B. She passed the tool over my teeth, cleaning them very well.

C. She used the tool to brush my teeth until they were very clean.

D. She gently scrubbed my teeth, slowly polishing them to bright white.

Unit 9 Test

🎧 LISTENING I

(Tracks 68–69) **You will hear a question. Then you will hear a conversation. After that, you will hear the question again and three choices. What is the correct answer: A, B, or C?**

1. A. cutting the after-school programs
    B. talking to other parents about the after-school programs
    C. making peer tutoring part of the after-school programs

2. A. getting a tutor
    B. studying more
    C. always doing her homework

🎧 LISTENING II

(Tracks 70–71) **You will hear the first part of a conversation. To finish the conversation, listen and choose the correct answer: A, B, or C.**

3. A. She's in second grade.
    B. She really likes science.
    C. She got a B.

4. A. Yes, here's my application.
    B. Yes, here's my electric bill.
    C. Yes, here's a note for my daughter's teacher.

🎧 LISTENING III

(Tracks 72–75) **You will hear a conversation. Then you will hear three sentences. Which sentence is true: A, B, or C?**

5. A. The man is involved in his children's education.
    B. The woman recommends getting involved in the children's education.
    C. The man asks how to get involved in his children's education.

6. A. The woman went to the PTA meeting.
    B. There's a PTA meeting next month.
    C. The man doesn't know what the PTA is.

7. A. The woman wants better equipment for the playground.
    B. The woman's son got hurt.
    C. The woman is concerned about safety on the playground.

8. A. The man can't go to parent-teacher night.
    B. The man wants to have a parent-teacher conference on Friday.
    C. The man can't have the conference on Friday because he has an appointment.

LIFE SKILLS

Read the next page and answer these questions. What is the correct answer: A, B, C, or D?

9. What are Paloma's two best classes?

    A. math and science

    B. computers and science

    C. math and language arts

    D. computers and math

10. What's Paloma's grade in social science?

    A. She got an A.

    B. She got a B.

    C. She got a C.

    D. She got a D.

11. In which of these areas does Paloma need to improve?

    A. respecting other students

    B. reading and writing

    C. doing her homework on time

    D. studying for math tests

12. Which of the following information is not given on this report card?

    A. comments about Paloma's work habits

    B. the classes Paloma is taking

    C. Paloma's grades from Reporting Period 1

    D. the number of days Paloma was late

Reporting Period 2

Student: Paloma Castro

Teacher: M. Richards

Number of days absent: 1

Number of days late: 2

Academics	Total Grade	Comments
Computers	97	Excels in all aspects of computers and technology
Mathematics	92	Has done an excellent job on all math assignments
Language Arts	75	Needs to improve reading and writing; needs to read more
Science	81	Has some trouble with science vocabulary
Social Science	73	Difficulty with reading affects ability to perform well
Habits & Attitudes		
Work Habits		
Completes all class and homework assignments		
Follows directions	X	Needs to pay attention to directions
Social Habits		
Shows respect for others		
Is responsible and reliable		
Works well in groups		
Assessment Key		
90–100 = A (Excellent)	60–69 = D (Poor)	
80–89 = B (Good)	Below 60 = F (Failing)	
70–79 = C (Average)	X = needs improvement	

GRAMMAR

Complete each conversation. What is the correct answer: A, B, or C?

13. **A:** The teachers were very _____ a lot of parents attended parent-teacher night.
    B: That *is* good news. It's important for parents to be involved in their children's education.

    A. pleased because
    B. pleased, and
    C. pleased so that

14. **A:** I made an appointment with Federico's teacher _____ we can talk to her about Federico's last report card.
    B: Good. When is the appointment? I'll need to request the time off from work.

    A. so that
    B. since
    C. to

15. **A:** Are you going to parent-teacher night this evening?
    B: Yes, I am. _____ I couldn't go last time, it's really important to be there tonight.

    A. So
    B. To
    C. Since

16. **A:** My kids' school sends home a calendar each month _____ let parents know about the events at the school.
    B: That's a great idea. I should suggest that at our next PTA meeting.

    A. because
    B. to
    C. so that

17. **A:** How is your son doing in school?
    B: He really likes it, but reading is hard for him. He's getting some tutoring _____ he's having some trouble.

    A. after school, so that
    B. after school since
    C. after school to

18. **A:** I'm interested in the free lunch program. Can you tell me how to apply?
    B: Sure. Here's the form _____ you need to fill out.

    A. since
    B. so that
    C. that

19. **A:** I'm so happy that my daughter is in Mrs. Richardson's class.
    B: I know. She's the kind of teacher _____ a difference in a child's life.

    A. makes
    B. who makes
    C. which makes

20. **A:** Do you and your husband both work?

    B: Yes. Our kids' school has an after-school program _____ both of us to work.

    A. which allows

    B. who allows

    C. because it allows

21. **A:** What are some things _____ parents can do to get more involved in their children's education?

    B: There are lots of ways to get involved. The easiest way is to ask your children every day, "How was school?"

    A. that

    B. so that

    C. who

22. **A:** Stephen has been having some social problems in school.

    B: Really? You should talk to one of the school's counselors. They're people _____ work with students, teachers, and parents to understand behavior problems.

    A. so that

    B. which

    C. who

23. **A:** Lorena wasn't at the safety meeting last night.

    B: I know. She had to work. She was going to try to trade shifts with someone, but she _____ able to.

    A. couldn't have been

    B. must not have been

    C. shouldn't have been

24. **A:** That science test was really hard!

    B: I know! I wish I had studied more. I _____ home and studied instead of going to a friend's house last night.

    A. may not have stayed

    B. must have stayed

    C. should have stayed

25. **A:** I wrote a note to Beto's teacher, and I asked Beto to give it to her. That was two days ago, and she hasn't called or written to me.

    B: She _____ the note. Maybe Beto forgot to give it to her.

    A. couldn't have gotten

    B. might not have gotten

    C. shouldn't have gotten

26. **A:** My daughter said that two girls got in a fight at school yesterday. She thought that one of them was Jenny Hills.

    B: Well, it _____ Jenny. She didn't go to school yesterday.

    A. couldn't have been

    B. shouldn't have been

    C. may not have been

27. **A:** I told Magali that I got a bad grade in English, and she told everyone!

    B: Well, you _____ her your grade. You know Magali can't keep a secret.

    A. must not have told

    B. might not have told

    C. shouldn't have told

READING I

Read. What is the correct answer: A, B, C, or D?

Commentary

Get Involved!

I'm concerned when I see children whose parents are not a part of their learning. I know that many parents have busy schedules and a lot of responsibilities. But as far as I can see, parents' biggest responsibility is helping their children get a good education. For children to do their best in school, I believe the involvement of every parent is essential.

Studies show that children whose parents are involved in their learning get better grades and have better behavior than other students. Getting involved doesn't have to be hard. Here are some ideas. First, read books with your children. It has been proven that reading to your children is the most important thing you can do to help them succeed in school. Second, talk to your children about school often, every day if possible. This will show them that education is important to you. Also, communicate regularly with your children's teachers. Discuss your children's progress and express any concerns you have.

It doesn't matter how much money or education you have—research shows that parents' involvement helps all children at all ages. Sure, parents are busy, and sometimes it's hard to find time to spend with your children. Sometimes you might have only a few minutes. But I believe that a child's education is more important than anything else. I think all parents should make time every day to be involved in their children's learning.

---

28. Which of the following sentences is an opinion?

A. I know that many parents have busy schedules and a lot of responsibilities.

B. As far as I can see, parents' biggest responsibility is helping their children get a good education.

C. Studies show that children whose parents are involved in their education get better grades.

D. It has been proven that reading to your children is the most important thing you can do to help them succeed in school.

29. Which of the following sentences is a fact?

A. For children to do their best in school, I believe the involvement of every parent is essential.

B. Research shows that parents' involvement helps all children at all ages.

C. I believe that a child's education is more important than anything else.

D. I think all parents should make time every day to be involved in their children's learning.

READING II

Read. What is the correct answer: A, B, C, or D?

Dear Ms. London,

I looked at my daughter Sofia's report card yesterday. I'm worried about her grades in language arts, science, and social science. I want to help her with her classes. Every day I ask Sofia about her homework, but she always says she doesn't need my help.

I want to be involved in Sofia's education. I'd like to schedule a conference with you to talk about how I can help her. Evenings are best for me so that I don't have to miss work, but I can be available during the day if that's better for you. Thank you for your help.

Sincerely,
Dasha Franko

30. What is the purpose of this note?

   A. to report a problem with Sofia's grades

   B. to ask Sofia's mother to make an appointment

   C. to request a conference with Sofia's teacher

   D. to ask a question about Sofia's homework

31. Why is Dasha Franko worried?

   A. She doesn't have time to help Sofia with her homework.

   B. Sofia has missed a lot of school.

   C. Sofia doesn't finish her homework.

   D. Sofia got bad grades in some classes.

WRITING

Read. What is the correct answer: A, B, C, or D?

Letter to the Editor:

As a mother of two students at Youngstown Elementary School, I think it's important for the children at that school to have good, quality equipment on the school playground. Last year there wasn't enough money for new playground equipment. And I was disappointed when the school announced that there won't be enough money in the budget for new equipment this year, either.

I understand that it would be expensive to replace all the playground equipment. However, I am concerned about the safety of the children who play on the old equipment that is there now. One possible solution is to organize teachers, students, and parents to raise money for new equipment.

Each classroom could choose one way to raise money, such as having a bake sale or selling sodas at school soccer games. A second possibility involves help from volunteers in the community. If the district can purchase the equipment, parents and other community members could volunteer to help take out the old equipment and put in the new pieces. That way the district would save money by not having to pay workers.

I plan to talk to the principal at Youngstown Elementary School and to other parents about these ideas at the PTA meeting next Wednesday at 7:00. I encourage interested parents to come to that meeting to share their thoughts.

32. Which of the following explains the organization of this letter?

   A. Paragraph 1 explains some advantages of new equipment. Paragraph 2 explains some disadvantages. Paragraph 3 asks for the reader's opinion.

   B. Paragraph 1 offers only opinions. Paragraph 2 states only facts. Paragraph 3 has suggestions.

   C. Paragraph 1 states the problem. Paragraph 2 gives solutions. Paragraph 3 describes next steps.

   D. Paragraph 1 identifies advantages and disadvantages. Paragraph 2 presents facts and opinions. Paragraph 3 offers solutions.

33. Which paragraph should this sentence be added to? *All opinions and ideas are welcome.*

   A. paragraph 1

   B. paragraph 2

   C. paragraph 3

   D. This sentence should start a new paragraph.

Unit 10 Test

🎧 LISTENING I

(Tracks 76–78) You will hear a question. Then you will hear a conversation. After that, you will hear the question again and three choices. What is the correct answer: A, B, or C?

1. A. to ask about the schedule
   B. to give a progress report
   C. to ask for a progress report

2. A. preventing an accident
   B. requirements for a promotion
   C. completing an accident report

3. A. just the woman
   B. the woman and the man
   C. the woman and Anna

🎧 LISTENING II

(Tracks 79–80) You will hear the first part of a conversation. To finish the conversation, listen and choose the correct answer: A, B, or C.

4. A. Not at all.
   B. Yes, I could.
   C. Thanks, but I don't need any help.

5. A. No problem. I'm glad to help.
   B. That would be great. Thanks a lot.
   C. Sorry, I'm busy.

🎧 LISTENING III

(Tracks 81–83) You will hear a conversation. Then you will hear three sentences. Which sentence is true: A, B, or C?

6. A. The woman always gets to work on time.
   B. The woman is getting a promotion.
   C. The woman is very efficient.

7. A. The woman has to wear a uniform.
   B. The woman is allowed to wear her own clothes.
   C. The woman prefers to wear a uniform.

8. A. The man's boss made him leave at 8:00.
   B. The man's boss let him leave at 8:00.
   C. The man got his boss to leave at 8:00.

LIFE SKILLS

Read the next page and answer these questions. What is the correct answer: A, B, C, or D?

9. Where did the accident happen?

   A. outside the building

   B. in the equipment room

   C. in Alina's office

   D. in the warehouse

10. How did Alina get hurt?

    A. She tripped on a big box.

    B. A big box fell on her.

    C. She tripped and fell.

    D. She fell off a ladder.

11. How long did Alina stay out of work?

    A. one day

    B. two days

    C. five days

    D. ten days

12. What did Natalie Cordova do?

    A. She caused the accident.

    B. She saw the accident.

    C. She borrowed Alina's safety equipment.

    D. She gave Alina medical treatment.

Accident Report Form

Use this form to report any work-related injuries. Complete the form immediately after the accident and submit it to your supervisor.

Employee Name: __Alina Federov__ ID Number: __2983764__

☐ Male　　☑ Female　　Date of Birth: __11/15/82__　Marital Status: __S__

Home Address: __2142 Kings Ave., Apt. 2C, Brooklyn, NY 11206__

Home Phone No. __718-555-3441__　Cell Phone No. __718-555-2017__

Job Title: _____

Employment Start Date: __12/1/08__

Date of Accident: __4/12/10__

Location of Accident: __22 Varick St, New York, NY 10013__

Describe in detail how the accident occurred (Describe the work you were engaged in, describe how the injury occurred, and explain the cause.):

> I was carrying a box through the warehouse. It was big, and I couldn't see over it or around it. As I was walking, I tripped. I dropped the box I was carrying, and I fell onto my hands and knees.

Part of body injured (Be specific: example: right middle finger, left ankle, upper back):
__left knee__

Type of injury (Example: sprain, burn [degree of burn], contusion, sutured):
__sprain__

Was medical treatment sought? If yes, person who provided treatment:
__Dr. Ramen, 872 Market St., Brooklyn, NY 11206　718-555-0029__

No. of days missed from work: __5__

Return to work date (as stated by physician): __4/19/10__

Type of leave used: __sick day__

No. of days worked with restrictions: __0__

Name of witness(es): __Natalie Cordova__

Phone No: __718-555-2693__

Was safety equipment provided?　　☑ Yes　　　　☐ No

Was safety equipment used?　☑ Yes　　　　☐ No

Signature of employee: __Alina Federov__　Date: __4/19/10__

GRAMMAR

Complete each conversation. What is the correct answer: A, B, or C?

13. **A:** Do you want to do something tonight? I was supposed to work until 9:00, but my boss _____ leave early today.

    B: That's great! Yeah, why don't we rent a movie?

    A. got me
    B. let me
    C. made

14. **A:** How are the work conditions at your new job?

    B: Good. Safety is very important to the company. They made _____ the company safety manual before I was allowed to work on the line.

    A. me read
    B. I read
    C. me to read

15. **A:** I thought you were running behind schedule.

    B: I was, but I had Ken _____ some other stores for the piece we needed. Now we're back on schedule.

    A. him to look at
    B. to look at
    C. look at

16. **A:** The company didn't want to pay extra to send the package by Express Mail, but I _____ to agree to it.

    B: That's great! How did you persuade them to do it?

    A. got them
    B. had them
    C. made them

17. **A:** The managers _____ all the employees work extra hours during the holiday season.

    B: Well, at least they got paid overtime.

    A. got
    B. let them
    C. had

18. **A:** Mr. Jones is pretty angry at Katarina because she accidentally broke the copy machine.

    B: Well, if it was an accident, then it wasn't her fault. He shouldn't blame _____.

    A. himself
    B. her
    C. herself

19. **A:** I can't believe you and Paul finished all this work! Did someone else help you?

    B: No, it took a while, but we did all of it _____.

    A. us
    B. our
    C. ourselves

20. **A:** Mariana and I want to learn how to operate the press.

B: OK, I can teach you. But you have to be careful so you don't hurt _____.

A. yourself
B. yourselves
C. you

21. **A:** Be careful on that ladder!

B: Thanks. Actually, could you please hold it for _____?

A. myself
B. yourself
C. me

22. **A:** Are you sure Pedro will remember to lock the doors before he leaves?

B: Yes. He wrote a note to _____ so that he wouldn't forget to do it.

A. himself
B. them
C. themselves

23. **A:** I feel terrible. I keep coughing and sneezing.

B: You're too sick to be at work! _____ go home and take care of yourself?

A. Could I
B. Why don't you
C. Would you mind

24. **A:** Hey, Arnold. _____ working for me this weekend? I'm on the schedule for Saturday, but it's my son's birthday.

B: Not at all. I could use the extra hours.

A. Could you
B. Why don't you
C. Would you mind

25. **A:** Hi, Kevin. This is Mr. Barnes. _____ give me a progress report on the house at 103 National Drive?

B: Sure. The subcontractor finished his work today, and we're still on schedule.

A. Why don't I
B. Could you
C. Could I

26. **A:** I don't know how to use the new computer program.

B: I learned how to use it last week. _____ show you how to use it?

A. Could you
B. Why don't I
C. Why don't you

27. **A:** Excuse me, Pablo. _____ take my break after I finish this?

B: Sure. That's fine.

A. Could I
B. Would you mind
C. Could you

READING I

Read. What is the correct answer: A, B, C, or D?

The Imperial Chicken Processing Plant Fire

In the 1980s, the Imperial chicken processing plant in Hamlet, North Carolina, was a terrible place to work. The plant was a factory for killing chickens and preparing their meat for sale. It was unsanitary and dangerous. The owners kept most of the doors and windows locked so that no one would steal the chickens. Many of the workers were unhappy with their work conditions, but no one complained or reported the problems. Hamlet was a town with few jobs and high unemployment. The workers knew that if they complained, the company could easily replace them.

Then on September 3, 1991, a fire broke out in the plant. Fifty-four people were injured, and sadly, twenty-five people died inside the plant. Those workers were trapped by the locked exit doors.

The fire was a big story in the news. People wanted to know why no one had enforced workplace health and safety laws. State and federal investigators later learned that there weren't enough inspectors in the state. Since there weren't enough inspectors and no one reported any problems, there had never been a safety inspection of the factory! One inspection could have prevented this terrible tragedy.

In 1992, the state of North Carolina passed fourteen new worker safety laws, including one that created a system for workers to report safety violations without fear of getting fired.

28. Which of the following happened first?

A. There was a fire at the Imperial chicken processing plant.

B. Employees at the plant didn't like their work conditions.

C. There were state and federal investigations.

D. North Carolina made new laws about worker safety.

29. Why didn't the workers complain about their work conditions?

A. They were afraid of getting caught stealing chickens.

B. They were afraid of the fire.

C. They were afraid of losing their jobs.

D. They were afraid of the safety inspectors.

READING II

Read. What is the correct answer: A, B, C, or D?

When she was eighteen, Coco never imagined that she could be someone's boss. That was two years ago, and Coco had just gotten a job as a dishwasher in a restaurant. She was working to earn some money to help her family. From the beginning, Coco was a good employee. And her boss was able to see this. Six months after Coco started, she was promoted to the position of waitress. Coco had more responsibility in that job, and she made more money. Coco continued to work hard for the next year and a half, and her hard work paid off: Two weeks ago the restaurant manager called her into his office for a talk. He told Coco she was an excellent worker, efficient, and accurate. And he complimented her especially for being able to work well with others. Then he announced that, for those reasons, he had decided to promote her to the position of assistant manager. Coco was thrilled. Yesterday was Coco's first day in her new position. She's excited about her new responsibilities, especially the opportunity to supervise other employees. She hopes she'll be a good boss! But most of all she is happy to know that she has earned a big promotion through her own hard work.

30. What is the main idea of this story?

    A. Coco will make a good assistant manager because she's a good employee.

    B. As an assistant manager, Coco is earning more money than when she first started working.

    C. Coco worked hard because she wanted to make more money.

    D. Through hard work, Coco is doing something that she didn't think was possible at one time.

31. According to the manager, why did Coco get a promotion?

    A. because she had worked at the restaurant for two years

    B. because she said she was interested in new opportunities

    C. because she was a very good worker

    D. because she had more responsibility in her job

WRITING

Read. What is the correct answer: A, B, C, or D?

TO:	Barbara Harris
FROM:	Frank Montero
SUBJECT:	Suggestion for improving warehouse safety and productivity

Dear Ms. Harris,

After working in the warehouse for four years, I've seen a lot of work-related injuries. I'd like to suggest a way to improve the health and safety of our warehouse employees. As you know, the workers in the warehouse often have to lift and carry big, heavy boxes. A lot of people aren't lifting them correctly, and they're getting injured. As a result, they have to take time off from work, or they have to work with restrictions. Either way, they're not as productive as they could be.

Many of the warehouse employees don't know that there are simple ways to prevent the most common injuries. For example, they may not know that when they bend down, they should keep their backs straight.

I suggest that the company provide a safety training session to all warehouse employees on how to prevent work-related injuries. Managers could show workers how to lift heavy boxes correctly. They could also show them how to use tools like a forklift for very heavy items. They could put up posters and signs around the warehouse to remind workers of the correct ways to lift and carry anything heavy.

I think this training session would be an easy and inexpensive way to improve safety and productivity in the warehouse.

Sincerely,
Frank Montero

32. According to the writer, what's the problem?

A. The workers have to lift and carry boxes that are very heavy.

B. The workers are taking too much time off work.

C. A lot of workers missed the safety training session.

D. Many workers are getting injured by lifting things incorrectly.

33. In which paragraph does the writer explain in detail the cause of the problem?

A. paragraph 1

B. paragraph 2

C. paragraph 3

D. paragraph 4

Unit 11 Test

🎧 LISTENING I

(Tracks 84–86) **You will hear a question. Then you will hear a conversation. After that, you will hear the question again and three choices. What is the correct answer: A, B, or C?**

1. A. Gabriela dropped and broke something in the store.
    B. Gabriela was in the store without permission.
    C. Someone left trash on the ground.

2. A. the robber
    B. the police
    C. several people

3. A. The woman was late.
    B. The woman was driving.
    C. The woman saw a fight.

🎧 LISTENING II

(Tracks 87–88) **You will hear the first part of a conversation. To finish the conversation, listen and choose the correct answer: A, B, or C.**

4. A. It's for $100.
    B. I got it in the mail.
    C. I got it for running a stop sign.

5. A. It's supposed to keep kids from being victims of crime.
    B. It's from 10 P.M. to 6 A.M.
    C. No kids under the age of eighteen are allowed downtown.

🎧 LISTENING III

(Tracks 89–91) **You will hear a conversation. Then you will hear three sentences. Which sentence is true: A, B, or C?**

6. A. The woman had to go to court.
    B. The woman borrowed money from her brother.
    C. The brothers went to court.

7. A. Edgar Casas asked about the crime scene.
    B. Edgar Casas described the crime scene.
    C. Edgar Casas was the lawyer for the defense.

8. A. There was no sign about parking on First Street.
    B. The man thinks the woman shouldn't have to pay the ticket.
    C. The woman cannot contest the ticket.

LIFE SKILLS I

Read each conversation and answer the questions. What is the correct answer: A, B, C, or D?

9. **A:** Carmen has to go to court tomorrow.
   B: Why? Is she in trouble?
   A: No, it's nothing like that. There was a robbery at a convenience store, and Carmen was in the parking lot when the robbers ran out. She has to tell everyone in court what she saw.

   Who is Carmen?

   A. She's the defendant.

   B. She's the bailiff.

   C. She's the court reporter.

   D. She's a witness.

10. **A:** Mr. Cordero, I'm not guilty. I didn't commit the crime!
    B: I believe you, Brian. I'm going to do everything I can to prove that you're innocent.

    Who is Mr. Cordero?

    A. the defense attorney

    B. the defendant

    C. the judge

    D. the prosecutor

LIFE SKILLS II

What is the correct answer: A, B, C, or D?

11. Which person in a trial is responsible for recording everything that is said during a trial?

    A. the jury

    B. the judge

    C. the court reporter

    D. the prosecutor

12. Which person in a trial would say the following: "We, the jury, find the defendant not guilty"?

    A. the defendant

    B. the bailiff

    C. the judge

    D. the foreman

GRAMMAR

Complete each conversation. What is the correct answer: A, B, or C?

13. **A:** I heard Alex got into trouble yesterday.

    B: Well, not really. He was sitting in front of an apartment building waiting for a friend _____. The security guard told Alex to leave. Alex explained the situation, and then there was no problem.

    A. when a security guard came by

    B. a security guard was coming by

    C. while a security guard was coming by

14. **A:** _____ through the park when a police officer stopped us. He said the park was closed.

    B: Well, the park officially closes at sunset. What time did the officer stop you?

    A. When we were walking

    B. We were walking

    C. While we were walking

15. **A:** _____, she heard a strange noise. She got scared, and she called the police.

    B: Then what happened?

    A. While my sister was babysitting

    B. When my sister babysat

    C. My sister was babysitting

16. **A:** I tried to call Stacy earlier, but she didn't answer the phone.

    B: You probably called _____ *New York Legal*. She loves that show so much that she never answers the phone when it's on.

    A. when she watched

    B. while she was watching

    C. she was watching

17. **A:** 911. What's your emergency?

    B: I want to report a crime. I'm in front of Main Bank on First Street. I was walking to my car _____ two men run out of the bank. They were carrying big bags. They got into a car, and they drove away very quickly.

    A. while I was seeing

    B. while I saw

    C. when I saw

18. **A:** Have you ever been called for jury duty?

    B: Yeah, I was on a jury last year. And I _____ to be the foreman.

    A. was chosen

    B. was choosing

    C. chosen

19. **A:** Dina _____ by a police officer on her way to work this morning.

    B: Why? Was she speeding?

    A. pulled over

    B. was pulled over

    C. was pulling over

20. **A:** Have you seen that new courtroom TV show on the Life channel?

 B: No. Is it any good?

 A: Yeah, it really is. Real people _____ to court, and the program follows their trials.

 A. brought

 B. are brought

 C. are bringing

21. **A:** How was your trip? Did you have any problems getting through customs?

 B: No, it went really well. An officer _____ us at customs. She searched our bags, but it didn't take long.

 A. was stopped

 B. stop

 C. stopped

22. **A:** Did a lot of people see the accident?

 B: Yes, and all of them _____ by the police.

 A. interview

 B. interviewed

 C. were interviewed

23. **A:** I'm really nervous about talking to the police.

 B: I understand. But you didn't do anything wrong. _____ you tell the truth, you won't have any problems.

 A. As long as

 B. Even if

 C. Even though

24. **A:** Are you allowed to make a left turn at a red light?

 B: No. _____ there's no other traffic, you always have to wait for a green light.

 A. Even though

 B. Even if

 C. As long as

25. **A:** _____ I'm in a hurry, I never speed.

 B: Really? Never?

 A: Never. It's not worth it to get a ticket, or worse, to get into an accident.

 A. Even though

 B. As long as

 C. Even if

26. **A:** Are teenagers allowed to be out after curfew if they're with their parents?

 B: Yes. _____ they're with a parent or responsible adult, there's no problem.

 A. Even though

 B. Even if

 C. As long as

27. **A:** Did the officer really give Sunar a ticket?

 B: Yes, he did. _____ Sunar explained that there was an emergency, he still got a speeding ticket.

 A. Even though

 B. As long as

 C. Even if

READING I

Read. What is the correct answer: A, B, C, or D?

DNA and Police Work

DNA is a relatively new discovery in the world of science, but it's quickly making a big difference in solving crimes. DNA is the most reliable way that police have to help prove a person's guilt or innocence.

No one else in the world has the same DNA as you. DNA is like a code that's just for you within your cells. Your DNA is in every cell of your body, including the cells of your hair, your skin, your blood, and your saliva.

Police can use DNA in different ways. When there is a crime, police collect evidence from the crime scene. They take samples of blood, hair, and anything else they find. Then, when police identify a suspect, or a person who they think committed the crime, they get a little bit of saliva from the person. Next, they get the samples they collected at the crime scene. They compare the DNA from the crime scene samples to the DNA of the suspect. When two DNA samples are compared, it's very easy to tell whether or not they came from the same person.

28. What is the main idea of this article?

A. No two people have the same DNA.

B. Police can take DNA samples from evidence at crime scenes.

C. DNA is a good way for police to help prove whether someone is innocent or guilty.

D. DNA can be found in blood, hair, and saliva.

29. Read this sentence again:
Then, when police identify a suspect, or a person who they think committed the crime, they get a little bit of saliva from the person.
Which of the following sentences has nearly the same meaning?

A. When a suspect commits a crime, policy identify him or her.

B. Police think that a suspect committed a crime because of the person's saliva.

C. Police match criminals to their saliva at the scene of a crime.

D. Police identify a suspect and then take saliva from that person.

READING II

Read. What is the correct answer: A, B, C, or D?

As of 2008, seventeen men in Dallas County, Texas, have been cleared of crimes they didn't commit and released from prison. After twenty-seven years in prison, James Woodard became one of those men.

In 1981, Woodard was wrongly accused of killing his girlfriend. The case went to trial, and although there was no real evidence, the jury found Woodard guilty. He was sent to prison.

Throughout the trial and his time in prison, Woodard always said that he didn't commit the crime. So what finally made the difference? An organization called the Innocent Project stepped in to help. They had the police compare evidence from the crime scene with Woodard's DNA. (At the time of the crime, DNA evidence was not yet used by police.) Mr. Woodard's DNA didn't match the DNA found at the scene of the crime. So, on April 29, 2008, state District Judge Mark Stoltz signed an order to release Woodard from prison.

Although Woodard will never get back the twenty-seven years he lost in prison for a crime he didn't commit, he's not angry. "Time is what you make of it," he says. "You're living no matter where you are. I think I came out pretty good. I think I won. I think I'm a winner."

---

30. Why did the judge decide that Mr. Woodard was innocent?

    A. Woodard's DNA was at the crime scene.

    B. Woodard's DNA was not the same as the DNA from the crime scene.

    C. The police found new evidence and used it to do DNA tests.

    D. Woodard was wrongly accused because of DNA evidence.

31. According to the article, how does James Woodard feel now that he's out of prison?

    A. He's sorry for committing the crime.

    B. He's angry about the time he lost in prison.

    C. He feels lonely because he doesn't have friends anymore.

    D. He has a positive attitude about the rest of his life.

WRITING

Read. Complete the sentences in the paragraph. What is the correct answer: A, B, C, or D?

The Rights of the Accused in the U.S. and Turkey

There are similarities and differences between the legal rights of accused people in the United States and in Turkey, my home country. In the United States, of course, a person who is accused of a crime has the right to a trial. Prosecutors and defense attorneys present the facts in court, and both of them try to prove their case. _____, when a
(32.)
person is accused of a crime in Turkey, he or she has a trial. In the United States, trials are heard by a jury. The jury listens to the evidence presented by both sides. The jury then decides the guilt or innocence of the person.
In contrast, _____.
(33.)
A judge (or in some cases, a group of judges) determines a defendant's guilt or innocence based on evidence presented in court.

32. Choose the word that correctly signals the sentence that follows it.

A. Similarly

B. Different

C. Like

D. In contrast

33. Choose the clause that should follow the phrase *In contrast.*

A. everyone in Turkey is allowed to have a trial by jury

B. there are no juries in the Turkish legal system

C. juries in Turkey decide if a person is innocent or guilty

D. the people on a Turkish jury listen to the evidence of a case

Unit 12 Test

🔊 LISTENING I

(Tracks 92–94) You will hear a question. Then you will hear a conversation. After that, you will hear the question again and three choices. What is the correct answer: A, B, or C?

1. A. get another job
    B. keep the job he has now
    C. give it all to charity

2. A. get the permits he needs
    B. fix up the building
    C. pass some inspections

3. A. visit her family
    B. stop going out so much
    C. buy a plane ticket

🔊 LISTENING II

(Tracks 95–96) You will hear the first part of a conversation. To finish the conversation, listen and choose the correct answer: A, B, or C.

4. A. my rent
    B. my budget
    C. my checking account

5. A. It's $500.
    B. It's 1 percent.
    C. There's no maintenance fee.

🔊 LISTENING III

(Tracks 97–99) You will hear a conversation. Then you will hear three sentences. Which sentence is true: A, B, or C?

6. A. The man has a job now.
    B. The man is planning to start college soon.
    C. The man already has a college degree.

7. A. The Advantage Checking Account is interest-free.
    B. The Advantage Checking Account requires a minimum balance.
    C. There are no fees for the Advantage Checking Account.

8. A. The woman's income is $1,000 a month.
    B. The woman owes $1,000.
    C. The woman's monthly credit card payment is $1,000.

LIFE SKILLS

Read the next page and answer these questions. What is the correct answer: A, B, C, or D?

9. What information is given in this W-2 form?

   A. Ada Rivera's earnings and the amount of tax she paid in 2008

   B. the amount of money that Ada Rivera will get back as a tax refund in 2008

   C. the amount that Ada Rivera and her husband will have to pay in taxes in 2008

   D. Ada Rivera's hourly pay and the number of hours she worked in 2008

10. What was Ada Rivera's total compensation in 2008?

    A. $23,106.00

    B. $11,553.00

    C. $470.21

    D. $267.99

11. What does the amount $2,458.09 represent on this W-2 form?

    A. the amount of Medicare tax withheld from Ada's pay

    B. the amount of state tax withheld from Ada's pay

    C. the amount of Social Security tax withheld from Ada's pay

    D. the amount of federal tax withheld from Ada's pay

12. Which of the following sentences is true?

    A. Ada Rivera didn't have a state ID number in 2008.

    B. Ada Rivera paid taxes to the Bertshire Hotel in 2008.

    C. Ada Rivera worked for the Bertshire Hotel in 2008.

    D. Ada Rivera didn't work in 2008.

a Employee's social security number 234-56-7890		OMB No. 2656-0007	Safe, accurate, FAST! Use	IRS e file	Visit the IRS website at www.irs.gov/efile.

b Employer identification number (EIN) 31-2907482	1 Wages, tips, other compensation $11,553.00	2 Federal income tax withheld $2,458.09
c Employer's name, address, and ZIP code **Bertshire Hotel** 2220 Wabash Ave. Dallas, TX 75202	3 Social security wages $11,553.00	4 Social security tax withheld $470.21
	5 Medicare wages and tips $11,553.00	6 Medicare tax withheld $267.99
	7 Social security tips	8 Allocated tips
d Control number	9 Advance EIC payment	10 Dependent care benefits

e Employee's first name and initial **Ada M.**	Last name **Rivera**	Suff.	11 Nonqualified plans	12a See instructions for box 12
			13 Statutory employee / Retirement plan / Third-party sick pay	12b
f Employee's address and ZIP code 1220 South Mason Rd. Dallas, TX 75203			14 Other	12c
				12d

15 State	Employer's state ID number 31-2907482	16 State wages, tips, etc. $11,553.00	17 State income tax $0	18 Local wages, tips, etc.	19 Local income tax	20 Locality name

Form **W-2** Wages and Tax statement **2008**

Copy B—to be filed with Employee's **FEDERAL** tax return.

GRAMMAR

Complete each conversation. What is the correct answer: A, B, or C?

13. **A:** How much interest do you earn on your checking account?
    B: None. It's _____ interest-free account.
    A. ∅
    B. an
    C. the

14. **A:** How would you like to pay for this, ma'am?
    B: I'll use _____ credit card. Which cards do you accept?
    A. the
    B. ∅
    C. a

15. **A:** UNICEF is a charity organization, isn't it?
    B: Yes. UNICEF stands for United Nations Children's Fund. _____ organization works to provide education, health care, and safety to children all over the world.
    A. An
    B. The
    C. ∅

16. **A:** People who always pay for things with _____ cash generally spend a lot less than people who use credit cards.
    B: Well, that makes sense. With credit cards, it's easy to spend a lot without realizing it.
    A. ∅
    B. a
    C. the

17. **A:** I got my W-2 form in the mail yesterday. I know I have to use it to do my taxes, but I don't know how.
    B: A lot of people think that _____ income tax forms are very complicated and hard to fill out. But they're really not that difficult. I can help you if you want.
    A. an
    B. the
    C. ∅

18. **A:** Would you like to get overdraft protection on your checking account? It's just $25 a month.
    B: No, thank you. If I _____ my balance carefully, I won't need it.
    A. watch
    B. watched
    C. will watch

19. **A:** I feel like I never have enough money, but I don't know what I spend it on.
    B: You should try recording all of your expenses for one month. If you write down everything you buy, _____ how you're spending your money.
    A. you'll see
    B. you would see
    C. you saw

20. **A:** Your English is really improving.
    B: Thanks. I've been taking classes and studying a lot. I _____ speak English well if I want to get a better job.

    A. had to
    B. would have to
    C. will have to

21. **A:** Kiki is thinking about taking some classes. She wants to get her GED.
    B: That's great. If she gets her GED, _____ more job opportunities.

    A. she'd have
    B. she'll have
    C. she has

22. **A:** Let's think about some ways we can reduce our expenses.
    B: Well, we'll save some money if we _____ the heat in the house.

    A. turn down
    B. would turn down
    C. turned down

23. **A:** One of my friends asked me to loan him $500. But that's a lot of money, and I'm worried he might have trouble paying me back.
    B: If I _____ you, I wouldn't lend him the money. Why don't you help him come up with a plan to earn or save the money on his own?

    A. will be
    B. were
    C. would be

24. **A:** Your wife is such a great cook. She should open a restaurant.
    B: Actually, that's her dream. _____ it tomorrow if she had the money.

    A. She did
    B. She'll do
    C. She would do

25. **A:** What _____ if you found $100 on the floor at work?
    B: I'd try to find out who it belonged to. That's what I would want someone to do for me.

    A. will you do
    B. would you do
    C. did you do

26. **A:** I know I should take my lunch to work, but I never feel like making it in the morning.
    B: Well, maybe you could do it the night before. You would save about $25 a week if you _____ your lunch instead of buying it at the cafeteria.

    A. took
    B. would take
    C. take

27. **A:** We really need to make a budget. If we had a plan for our money, we _____ better decisions about our spending.
    B: I agree. Let's work on one this weekend.

    A. made
    B. will make
    C. would make

READING I

Read. What is the correct answer: A, B, C, or D?

Living the Dream

When Tina Mendez looked at the empty storefront with the "for rent" sign, she didn't see an empty space. Instead, she imagined a bakery humming with business. That was her dream—to own her own bakery.

It wasn't easy to start her business. There were a lot of forms to fill out in order to register her business with the state and get a business license. And of course, she needed money to buy refrigerators, ovens, and other equipment. She didn't want to borrow from her friends or relatives, so she got a bank loan. Then, before she could open her doors, she was required to pass seven different inspections. She didn't pass some of them the first time.

But eventually, after some improvements, she passed all of them. She was finally ready for business.

Once the bakery opened, Tina had to attract customers. She hired her niece to offer free samples to people walking by the bakery. Everyone loved them. Little by little, customers started telling other people about Tina's delicious cakes, cookies, and breads. The business started to grow.

That was two years ago. Tina has started to pay back the money she borrowed from the bank. She hired her niece to work full time, and she hired a few part-time employees, too. Business is going well, and Tina is living her dream.

28. Which of the following is the best summary of this article?

   A. Tina's dream was to own her own bakery. She thought about it a lot. She found an empty storefront, and she imagined starting her bakery there. At first, she gave away free samples. It was a good idea because she got a lot of new customers that way. Now her bakery is successful.

   B. Tina worked hard to start her business. She had to fill out a lot of forms to get licensed. She had to get a bank loan so she could buy equipment. And she had to pass many different inspections. Finally, Tina opened the bakery and started to attract customers. Today she has a successful bakery.

   C. It was hard for Tina to start her own business. She needed a lot of help from her niece. In the beginning, her niece helped by giving out samples. Today, she's a full-time employee. Tina hired some other employees, too, but they work part time.

   D. Two years ago Tina wanted to start a business. But she needed money, and she didn't want to ask her friends or family for help. So she had to go to the bank and get a loan. Now she's making money at her business, and she's paying back the loan.

29. How does Tina probably feel now?

   A. She's proud that she has paid back all the money to the bank.

   B. She's worried about passing all seven inspections.

   C. She's happy because she made her dream come true.

   D. She's excited because she's going to open another bakery.

READING II

Read. What is the correct answer: A, B, C, or D?

A few years ago, Tram Lang got a credit card. It was great—he could buy almost anything he wanted, and he could pay for it later! But after just a few months, Tram had bought too many things with his credit card. He couldn't pay the full amount of his monthly bill, so he only paid part of it. The credit card company charged him interest on the balance.

Tram realized he was in trouble: He owed the credit card company a lot of money. So he made some important decisions and some big changes. He stopped using his credit card. Tram opened a checking account, and he started to use his debit card instead of his credit card. He watched his balance carefully to make sure he never wrote a check, made a purchase, or made an online payment for more than the amount in his account. Every month he paid the credit card company as much as he could. After a year, Tram finally paid off the balance on his credit card.

Today Tram still has his credit card, but he only uses it for big purchases. He uses his debit card to buy smaller things.

30. What is the main idea of this story?

    A. Tram didn't have a lot of money in his bank account, so he used his credit card to buy things.

    B. Tram used his debit card instead of his credit card after he opened his bank account.

    C. Today Tram doesn't usually use his credit card.

    D. After he got into trouble with his credit card, Tram made some positive changes.

31. What was Tram's problem?

    A. He didn't earn enough interest on his checking account.

    B. He used his credit card too much, and he owed the company a lot of money.

    C. The bank was charging Tram too much interest on his account.

    D. Tram made debit card purchases for more than the amount he had in his account.

WRITING

Read. What is the correct answer: A, B, C, or D?

So, you'd like to give some money to a charity. But maybe you don't have a lot of extra money to give. _____
(32.)

The answer is simple: Get creative! You don't always need a lot of money to make money. For example, you can raise money by having a car wash. Get some of your friends, neighbors, or coworkers together. Buy (or borrow) your supplies: buckets, soap, sponges, towels, etc. If you spend $50 on supplies and charge $10 per car, then you'll only need to wash five cars before you make your money back. The rest of the money you earn goes to charity. Here's another idea: Sell your talents. Some parents in the PTA at my son's school decided to bake to make money. They each gave $20 to buy ingredients. Then they made cookies and sold them to other parents and teachers at a PTA meeting. They made over $300! So don't limit yourself. Think how you could use your ideas and talents to raise money for your favorite charity.

32. Which question should the writer ask to best focus this paragraph?

A. How can you become active in a charity in your area?

B. If you had $1 million to give to a charity, which one would you choose?

C. How can you choose which charity to support?

D. What are some good ways to raise money for charity?

33. The answer to the writer's question is "Get creative." Which of the following sentences helps explain the answer by providing an example?

A. You don't always need a lot of money to make money.

B. You can raise money by having a car wash.

C. The rest of the money you earn goes to charity.

D. They made over $300!

Future 4
Unit Test Answer Sheet

① _____
   Last Name   First Name   Middle

② _____
   Teacher's Name

TEST

1 (A) (B) (C) (D)
2 (A) (B) (C) (D)
3 (A) (B) (C) (D)
4 (A) (B) (C) (D)
5 (A) (B) (C) (D)
6 (A) (B) (C) (D)
7 (A) (B) (C) (D)
8 (A) (B) (C) (D)
9 (A) (B) (C) (D)
10 (A) (B) (C) (D)
11 (A) (B) (C) (D)
12 (A) (B) (C) (D)
13 (A) (B) (C) (D)
14 (A) (B) (C) (D)
15 (A) (B) (C) (D)
16 (A) (B) (C) (D)
17 (A) (B) (C) (D)
18 (A) (B) (C) (D)
19 (A) (B) (C) (D)
20 (A) (B) (C) (D)
21 (A) (B) (C) (D)
22 (A) (B) (C) (D)
23 (A) (B) (C) (D)
24 (A) (B) (C) (D)
25 (A) (B) (C) (D)
26 (A) (B) (C) (D)
27 (A) (B) (C) (D)
28 (A) (B) (C) (D)
29 (A) (B) (C) (D)
30 (A) (B) (C) (D)
31 (A) (B) (C) (D)
32 (A) (B) (C) (D)
33 (A) (B) (C) (D)

Directions for marking answers

- Use a No. 2 pencil. Do NOT use ink.
- Make dark marks and bubble in your answers completely.
- If you change an answer, erase your first mark completely.

Right
(A) (B) (C) (D)

Wrong
(A) (X) (C) (D)
(A) (B) (C) (D)

③ STUDENT IDENTIFICATION

0	0	0	0	0	0	0	0	0	0
1	1	1	1	1	1	1	1	1	1
2	2	2	2	2	2	2	2	2	2
3	3	3	3	3	3	3	3	3	3
4	4	4	4	4	4	4	4	4	4
5	5	5	5	5	5	5	5	5	5
6	6	6	6	6	6	6	6	6	6
7	7	7	7	7	7	7	7	7	7
8	8	8	8	8	8	8	8	8	8
9	9	9	9	9	9	9	9	9	9

Is this your Social Security number?
Yes ( )   No ( )

④ TEST DATE

MM		D	D	Y	Y
Jan ( )		0	0	200	9
Feb ( )		1	1	201	0
Mar ( )		2	2	201	1
Apr ( )		3	3	201	2
May ( )			4	201	3
Jun ( )			5	201	4
Jul ( )			6	201	5
Aug ( )			7	201	6
Sep ( )			8	201	7
Oct ( )			9	201	8
Nov ( )					
Dec ( )					

⑤ CLASS NUMBER

0	0	0	0	0	0	0	0
1	1	1	1	1	1	1	1
2	2	2	2	2	2	2	2
3	3	3	3	3	3	3	3
4	4	4	4	4	4	4	4
5	5	5	5	5	5	5	5
6	6	6	6	6	6	6	6
7	7	7	7	7	7	7	7
8	8	8	8	8	8	8	8
9	9	9	9	9	9	9	9

⑥ RAW SCORE

0	0
1	1
2	2
3	3
4	4
5	5
6	6
7	7
8	8
9	9

Unit 1 Test Answer Key

	ANSWER	LESSON/PAGE	OBJECTIVE
1	(A) B (C) (D)	4/p. 12	Understand a conversation about goals
2	(A) (B) (C) (D)	8/p. 20	Understand a conversation about people's past experiences
3	(A) B (C) (D)	2/p. 8	Understand a conversation about routines
4	(A) (B) (C) (D)	8/p. 20	Understand a conversation about people's past experiences
5	(A) (B) C (D)	4/p. 12	Understand a conversation about goals
6	(A) (B) (C) (D)	1/p. 6	Understand a conversation about a person and his or her family
7	(A) (B) C (D)	2/p. 9	Understand a conversation about routines
8	(A) (B) C (D)	5/p. 14	Understand a conversation about goals
9	(A) (B) (C) (D)	6/p. 17	Interpret a school application
10	(A) (B) C (D)	6/p. 16	Interpret a school application
11	(A) (B) (C) (D)	6/p. 16	Interpret a school application
12	(A) B (C) (D)	6/p. 16	Interpret a school application
13	(A) (B) (C) (D)	2/p. 8	Simple present and present continuous
14	(A) (B) C (D)	2/p. 8	Simple present and present continuous
15	(A) B (C) (D)	2/p. 8	Simple present and present continuous
16	(A) (B) (C) (D)	2/p. 8	Simple present and present continuous
17	(A) (B) C (D)	2/p. 8	Simple present and present continuous
18	(A) B (C) (D)	5/p. 15	Future with *will, be going to,* and present continuous
19	(A) (B) (C) (D)	5/p. 14	Future with *will, be going to,* and present continuous
20	(A) (B) (C) (D)	5/p. 14	Future with *will, be going to,* and present continuous
21	(A) B (C) (D)	5/p. 14	Future with *will, be going to,* and present continuous
22	(A) B (C) (D)	5/p. 14	Future with *will, be going to,* and present continuous
23	(A) (B) C (D)	8/p. 20	Simple past
24	(A) (B) (C) (D)	8/p. 20	Simple past
25	(A) (B) C (D)	8/p. 20	Simple past
26	(A) B (C) (D)	8/p. 21	*Used to*
27	(A) (B) (C) (D)	8/p. 21	*Used to*
28	(A) (B) (C) (D)	3/p. 10	Identify the main idea
29	(A) (B) C (D)	3/p. 10	Understand details
30	(A) (B) (C) (D)	3/p. 10	Understand details
31	(A) (B) C (D)	3/p. 10	Understand details
32	(A) (B) C (D)	6/p. 16	Use chronological order
33	(A) (B) C (D)	6/p. 16	Use chronological order

Please see reverse for test Audio Script.

Unit 1 Test Audio Script

Listening I (Tracks 3–5) Page 1.

1. What is the man talking about?
   F: What are you reading?
   M: Some information I got from a technical school. I want to take some classes.
   F: That's great.
   M: Yeah. I'm excited about it. I'm going to visit a few schools, and I'll send my applications next month.

   What is the man talking about?

2. What did the man do a lot in the past?
   M: I never used to take public transportation. I used to drive my car everywhere.
   F: But now you take the bus?
   M: Yes. And I like it better. Now I read and relax more.

   What did the man do a lot in the past?

3. What is the woman's usual work schedule?
   M: Do you always work in the mornings?
   F: No, I usually work in the evenings. But today I'm working for Michelle. She's going to the doctor this morning, so I'm taking her shift.

   What is the woman's usual work schedule?

Listening II (Tracks 6–7) Page 1.

4. **F:** I'm from Poland. I grew up there.
   M: Oh. Did you work there before you came to the United States?

5. **M:** I don't want to drive a truck my whole life. I want to do something different.
   F: So what are your goals for the future?

Listening III (Tracks 8–10) Page 1.

6. **F:** So how's everything going? Where are you living now?
   M: In an apartment on Second Avenue. It's small, especially with two kids. But we like living in the city.

   Which sentence is true?

7. **M:** How do you spend your weekends?
   F: Well, during the week I don't usually have time to relax. So on weekends I like to stay home and read or watch TV.

   Which sentence is true?

8. **F1:** I saw Olga the other day. She's going to go back to school.
   F2: Really?
   F1: Yeah. She's starting classes next month.

   Which sentence is true?

Unit 2 Test Answer Key

	ANSWER	LESSON/PAGE	OBJECTIVE
1	A **B** C D	8/p. 40	Understand a conversation about previous work experience and duties
2	A **B** C D	1/p. 26	Understand a conversation about work-related goals
3	A **B** C D	1/p. 26	Understand a conversation about work-related goals
4	**A** B C D	5/p. 34	Understand a conversation about job-related skills and abilities
5	A B **C** D	8/p. 40	Understand a conversation about previous work experience and duties
6	A **B** C D	8/p. 40	Understand a conversation about previous work experience and duties
7	A **B** C D	1/p. 26	Understand a conversation about work-related goals
8	**A** B C D	4/p. 32	Understand a conversation about using job-information sources
9	**A** B C D	3/p. 30	Interpret a resume
10	A B C **D**	3/p. 30	Interpret a resume
11	A **B** C D	3/p. 30	Interpret a resume
12	A B **C** D	3/p. 30	Interpret a resume
13	**A** B C D	2/p. 28	Infinitives and gerunds
14	**A** B C D	2/p. 28	Infinitives and gerunds
15	**A** B C D	2/p. 28	Infinitives and gerunds
16	A B **C** D	2/p. 28	Infinitives and gerunds
17	**A** B C D	2/p. 28	Infinitives and gerunds
18	A **B** C D	5/p. 34	Gerunds as objects of preposition
19	A B **C** D	5/p. 34	Gerunds as objects of preposition
20	A **B** C D	5/p. 34	Gerunds as objects of preposition
21	A B **C** D	5/p. 34	Gerunds as objects of preposition
22	**A** B C D	5/p. 34	Gerunds as objects of preposition
23	A B **C** D	5/p. 34	Simple past and present perfect
24	**A** B C D	5/p. 40	Simple past and present perfect
25	A **B** C D	8/p. 40	Simple past and present perfect
26	**A** B C D	8/p. 40	Simple past and present perfect
27	A **B** C D	8/p. 40	Simple past and present perfect
28	**A** B C D	6/p. 36	Understand details
29	A B C **D**	6/p. 36	Understand details
30	A B C **D**	6/p. 36	Identify the main idea
31	A B C **D**	6/p. 36	Understand details
32	A B **C** D	9/p. 42	Write a cover letter
33	A B C **D**	9/p. 42	Include appropriate information in a cover letter

Please see reverse for test Audio Script.

Unit 2 Test Audio Script

Listening I (Tracks 11–13) Page 9.

1. What is the man talking about?
   F: Tell me about the jobs you've had.
   M: Well, right now I'm a waiter at a restaurant. Before that, I worked at a grocery store. I was a clerk.

   What is the man talking about?

2. What does the woman want to do in the future?
   M: So, what do you do?
   F: I work part time, and I take computer classes. My goal is to get a job as an office assistant.

   What does the woman want to do in the future?

3. What is the woman going to do in a year?
   M: Did you finish school?
   F: Not yet. I studied for two years in Brazil. But then I came to the U.S. I plan to complete my degree in a year, in night school.

   What is the woman going to do in a year?

Listening II (Tracks 14–15) Page 9.

4. **F:** I have experience working in an office.
   M: OK. That's good. Tell me about your skills.

5. **F:** I work in a warehouse right now.
   M: OK. And how long have you had your current job?

Listening III (Tracks 16–18) Page 9.

6. **F:** Where do you work now, and what other jobs have you had?
   M: Well, my current job is in a factory. Before that, I was a dishwasher at a restaurant.

   Which sentence is true?

7. **M:** What kind of job are you looking for?
   F: I don't know. I'm interested in fashion.
   M: Here's a job at a clothing store. You should call them.

   Which sentence is true?

8. **M:** How's the job hunt going?
   F: OK. So far, I've sent out my résumé online, and I've been to an employment agency.

   Which sentence is true?

Unit 3 Test Answer Key

	ANSWER	LESSON/PAGE	OBJECTIVE
1	A B **C** D	1/p. 46	Understand a conversation about cultural festivals and traditions
2	A B **C** D	7/p. 57	Understand a conversation about ways to improve a community
3	A **B** C D	2/p. 48	Understand a conversation about feelings about a neighborhood
4	**A** B C D	2/p. 48	Understand a conversation about feelings about a neighborhood
5	A B **C** D	2/p. 48	Understand a conversation about feelings about a neighborhood
6	A **B** C D	8/p. 60	Understand a conversation about community problems
7	A **B** C D	5/p. 54	Understand a conversation about making changes in a community
8	**A** B C D	4/p. 52	Understand a conversation about community issues
9	A B **C** D	3/p. 50	Understand a conversation about community center activities
10	A B C **D**	3/p. 50	Understand a conversation about community center activities
11	**A** B C D	3/p. 50	Understand a conversation about getting and following directions
12	A **B** C D	3/p. 50	Understand a conversation about getting and following directions
13	A **B** C D	2/p. 48	Participial adjectives
14	A B **C** D	2/p. 48	Participial adjectives
15	A B C **D**	2/p. 48	Participial adjectives
16	**A** B C D	2/p. 48	Participial adjectives
17	**A** B C D	2/p. 48	Participial adjectives
18	**A** B C D	5/p. 54	*Wish* in the present and future
19	**A** B C D	5/p. 54	*Wish* in the present and future
20	A B **C** D	5/p. 54	*Wish* in the present and future
21	A **B** C D	5/p. 54	*Wish* in the present and future
22	**A** B C D	5/p. 54	*Wish* in the present and future
23	A B **C** D	8/p. 60	Verb + object + infinitive
24	**A** B C D	8/p. 60	Verb + object + infinitive
25	**A** B C D	8/p. 60	Verb + object + infinitive
26	**A** B C D	8/p. 60	Verb + object + infinitive
27	A B **C** D	8/p. 60	Verb + object + infinitive
28	A B C **D**	6/p. 56	Make inferences
29	A B **C** D	6/p. 56	Understand details
30	A B C **D**	6/p. 56	Identify the main idea
31	A B C **D**	6/p. 56	Identify the main idea
32	A B C **D**	9/p. 62	Use examples to give details in writing
33	A **B** C D	9/p. 62	Use examples to give details in writing

Please see reverse for test Audio Script.

Unit 3 Test Audio Script

Listening I (Tracks 19–20) Page 17.

1. What is the man talking about?
   M: I love the Mexican Festival. I go every year.
   F: Really? What's it like?
   M: It's fun. There's traditional music and dancing. And there are lots of stands with typical Mexican crafts and food.

   What is the man talking about?

2. What does the man want?
   M: I wish there were more public transportation in this city.
   F: I know. That would be great. I like my car, but I don't like all the traffic.

   What does the man want?

Listening II (Tracks 21–22) Page 17.

3. **F:** You live in Oak Park, right? How do you feel about your neighborhood?

4. **M:** What do you think of the downtown part of the city?

Listening III (Tracks 23–26) Page 17.

5. **F:** How does your sister like her neighborhood?
   M: It's OK. But she doesn't speak English well, and she's embarrassed.

   Which sentence is true?

6. **M:** Police are urging people to check on their neighbors.
   F: OK, I'll go to Mrs. Madison's house after dinner.

   Which sentence is true?

7. **M:** Will you go with me to the community meeting?
   F: Not tonight. I'm busy.
   M: Come on! This meeting is important. It's our chance to make a difference in the community.

   Which sentence is true?

8. **M:** I wish there weren't so many potholes in the roads.
   F: I know. They're terrible. I wish the community would fix them.

   Which sentence is true?

Life Skills (Track 27) Page 18.

See page 123 for the audio script for Life Skills (Track 27).

Unit 4 Test Answer Key

	ANSWER	LESSON/PAGE	OBJECTIVE
1	Ⓐ Ⓑ **Ⓒ** Ⓓ	8/p. 80	Understand a conversation about following work-related instructions
2	**Ⓐ** Ⓑ Ⓒ Ⓓ	1/p. 66	Understand a conversation about communicating at work
3	Ⓐ **Ⓑ** Ⓒ Ⓓ	2/p. 68	Understand a conversation about communicating at work
4	Ⓐ Ⓑ **Ⓒ** Ⓓ	5/p. 74	Understand a conversation checking understanding of a situation
5	**Ⓐ** Ⓑ Ⓒ Ⓓ	2/p. 68	Understand a conversation at work
6	Ⓐ Ⓑ **Ⓒ** Ⓓ	4/p. 72	Understand a conversation checking understanding of a situation
7	Ⓐ **Ⓑ** Ⓒ Ⓓ	4/p. 72	Understand a conversation checking understanding of a situation
8	Ⓐ Ⓑ **Ⓒ** Ⓓ	6/p. 76	Understand a conversation about common workplace injuries
9	Ⓐ Ⓑ **Ⓒ** Ⓓ	3/p. 70	Interpret information about employee benefits
10	**Ⓐ** Ⓑ Ⓒ Ⓓ	3/p. 70	Interpret information about employee benefits
11	Ⓐ Ⓑ Ⓒ **Ⓓ**	3/p. 70	Interpret information about employee benefits
12	Ⓐ **Ⓑ** Ⓒ Ⓓ	3/p. 70	Interpret information about employee benefits
13	Ⓐ **Ⓑ** Ⓒ Ⓓ	2/p. 68	Phrasal verbs
14	**Ⓐ** Ⓑ Ⓒ Ⓓ	2/p. 68	Phrasal verbs
15	Ⓐ Ⓑ **Ⓒ** Ⓓ	2/p. 68	Phrasal verbs
16	Ⓐ Ⓑ **Ⓒ** Ⓓ	2/p. 68	Phrasal verbs
17	**Ⓐ** Ⓑ Ⓒ Ⓓ	2/p. 68	Phrasal verbs
18	**Ⓐ** Ⓑ Ⓒ Ⓓ	5/p. 74	Negative *yes/no* questions
19	Ⓐ Ⓑ **Ⓒ** Ⓓ	5/p. 74	Negative *yes/no* questions
20	Ⓐ Ⓑ **Ⓒ** Ⓓ	5/p. 74	Negative *yes/no* questions
21	**Ⓐ** Ⓑ Ⓒ Ⓓ	5/p. 74	Negative *yes/no* questions
22	Ⓐ **Ⓑ** Ⓒ Ⓓ	5/p. 74	Negative *yes/no* questions
23	**Ⓐ** Ⓑ Ⓒ Ⓓ	8/p. 80	Indirect instructions, commands, and requests
24	Ⓐ Ⓑ **Ⓒ** Ⓓ	8/p. 80	Indirect instructions, commands, and requests
25	Ⓐ Ⓑ **Ⓒ** Ⓓ	8/p. 80	Indirect instructions, commands, and requests
26	**Ⓐ** Ⓑ Ⓒ Ⓓ	8/p. 80	Indirect instructions, commands, and requests
27	Ⓐ **Ⓑ** Ⓒ Ⓓ	8/p. 80	Indirect instructions, commands, and requests
28	Ⓐ Ⓑ **Ⓒ** Ⓓ	6/p. 76	Recognize restatements
29	Ⓐ Ⓑ **Ⓒ** Ⓓ	6/p. 76	Understand details
30	Ⓐ Ⓑ **Ⓒ** Ⓓ	7/p. 78	Identify the main idea
31	Ⓐ Ⓑ **Ⓒ** Ⓓ	7/p. 78	Understand details
32	Ⓐ **Ⓑ** Ⓒ Ⓓ	9/p. 82	Write a memo to a supervisor
33	Ⓐ Ⓑ Ⓒ **Ⓓ**	9/p. 82	Write a memo to a supervisor

Please see reverse for test Audio Script.

Unit 4 Test Audio Script

Listening I (Tracks 28–30) Page 24.

1. What did the supervisor tell the woman to do?
   M: How was your performance review?
   F: It was fine. The supervisor said I follow safety procedures well. But she told me to ask questions if I'm not sure what to do.

   What did the supervisor tell the woman to do?

2. What does the man need to do?
   F: There's a lot to learn, but you're picking it up quickly. Let me know if there's any way I can help you out.
   M: Thanks. Right now, I need to find out about my vacation days.

   What does the man need to do?

3. What should the woman do?
   M: Please point out the problems to me.
   F: OK. I will.

   What should the woman do?

Listening II (Tracks 31–32) Page 24.

4. **F:** Here's the list of supplies we need to order.
   M: Thanks…. Hmm. I don't see pens on the list. Don't we need pens?

5. **M:** Hey, my performance review is today.
   F: I know. Are you still nervous?

Listening III
(Tracks 33–35) Page 24.

6. **M:** Are you going to leave early next Friday before the holiday?
   F: Well, I'd like to, but doesn't someone have to be here to receive the afternoon shipment?

   Which sentence is true?

7. **F:** Hasn't anyone given this information to the doctor?
   M: No, no one has. But I can do it right now.

   Which sentence is true?

8. **F:** Ow, my hand really hurts. Every time I pick up the telephone I get pain down my hand. It started at work last week.
   M: I'm sorry. That sounds like you have a repetitive stress injury. Maybe you should use a headset so you can give your hand a rest.

   Which sentence is true?

Unit 5 Test Answer Key

	ANSWER	LESSON/PAGE	OBJECTIVE
1	A **B** C D	1/p. 86	Understand a conversation about ways to prevent fires
2	A B **C** D	4/p. 92	Understand a conversation about dangerous weather
3	A B **C** D	7/p. 98	Understand a conversation about a 911 emergency
4	A B **C** D	2/p. 86	Understand a conversation about what to do in case of fire
5	**A** B C D	4/p. 92	Understand a conversation about dangerous weather
6	**A** B C D	7/p. 98	Understand a conversation about a 911 emergency
7	A **B** C D	6/p. 96	Understand a conversation about planning for a hurricane
8	A **B** C D	4/p. 92	Understand a conversation about dangerous weather
9	A B **C** D	6/p. 97	Interpret an evacuation map
10	A **B** C D	6/p. 97	Interpret an evacuation map
11	**A** B C D	6/p. 97	Interpret an evacuation map
12	A B C **D**	6/p. 97	Interpret an evacuation map
13	**A** B C D	2/p. 86	Present real conditionals
14	A B **C** D	2/p. 86	Present real conditionals
15	**A** B C D	2/p. 86	Present real conditionals
16	A **B** C D	2/p. 86	Present real conditionals
17	A B **C** D	2/p. 86	Present real conditionals
18	A **B** C D	5/p. 94	Adverb clauses of time
19	A **B** C D	5/p. 94	Adverb clauses of time
20	**A** B C D	5/p. 94	Adverb clauses of time
21	A **B** C D	5/p. 94	Adverb clauses of time
22	A B **C** D	5/p. 94	Adverb clauses of time
23	**A** B C D	8/p. 100	Expressing degrees of certainty
24	**A** B C D	8/p. 100	Expressing degrees of certainty
25	A B **C** D	8/p. 100	Expressing degrees of certainty
26	A B **C** D	8/p. 100	Expressing degrees of certainty
27	**A** B C D	8/p. 100	Expressing degrees of certainty
28	A **B** C D	3/p. 90	Identify the main idea
29	A B C **D**	3/p. 90	Identify an author's purpose
30	A B **C** D	3/p. 90	Understand details
31	**A** B C D	3/p. 90	Understand details
32	A **B** C D	9/p. 102	Use a logical order to write about steps in a process
33	A B C **D**	9/p. 102	Use a logical order to write about steps in a process

Please see reverse for test Audio Script.

Unit 5 Test Audio Script

Listening I (Tracks 36–37) Page 32.

1. What information does the man give?
   F: I want to keep my home safe from fires. What do you recommend?
   M: There are many ways to improve fire safety in your home. For example, you can ask people to smoke outside.

   What information does the man give?

2. What are the people talking about?
   F: What should I do when there's a thunderstorm?
   M: You should get inside a building as soon as you see lightning. Stay inside until the thunderstorm ends.

   What are the people talking about?

Listening II (Tracks 38–39) Page 32.

3. **M:** 911. What's your emergency?

4. **F:** What should I do if there's a fire in my home?

Listening III (Tracks 40–43) Page 32.

5. **F:** It's been raining all day!
   M: I know. Be careful when you're driving. The roads could be dangerous.

   Which sentence is true?

6. **M:** 911. What's your emergency?
   F: A man is having an allergic reaction. He's having trouble breathing, and he needs help.

   Which sentence is true?

7. **F:** I just heard about the hurricane on the weather report. Are you OK?
   M: Yes, but the hurricane is coming towards us! I'm getting ready so I can leave the house. It's not safe to stay in this area.

   Which sentence is true?

8. **M:** Can you believe this weather?
   F: It's been really bad lately. Now there's a hurricane watch for this area.

   Which sentence is true?

Unit 6 Test Answer Key

	ANSWER	LESSON/PAGE	OBJECTIVE
1	A (B) **C** (D)	2/p. 108	Understand a conversation about tenant responsibilities
2	A **(B)** C D	4/p. 112	Understand a conversation about landlord responsibilities
3	A **(B)** C D	7/p. 118	Understand a conversation about problems with neighbors
4	**A** B C D	2/p. 108	Understand a conversation about tenant responsibilities
5	A **B** C D	3/p. 110	Understand a conversation about a lease
6	A B **C** D	2/p. 108	Understand a conversation about tenant responsibilities
7	**A** B C D	4/p. 112	Understand a conversation about landlord responsibilities
8	**A** B C D	7/p. 118	Understand a conversation about problems with neighbors
9	A B C **D**	3/p. 110	Interpret a lease
10	A B **C** D	3/p. 110	Interpret a lease
11	A **B** C D	3/p. 110	Interpret a lease
12	A B C **D**	3/p. 110	Interpret a lease
13	**A** B C D	2/p. 108	Expressing expectation and permission
14	A **B** C D	2/p. 108	Expressing expectation and permission
15	A **B** C D	2/p. 108	Expressing expectation and permission
16	A B **C** D	2/p. 108	Expressing expectation and permission
17	A B **C** D	2/p. 108	Expressing expectation and permission
18	**A** B C D	5/p. 114	Tag questions with *do* as an auxiliary verb
19	A B **C** D	5/p. 114	Tag questions with *do* as an auxiliary verb
20	**A** B C D	5/p. 114	Tag questions with *be*
21	A **B** C D	5/p. 114	Tag questions with *do* as an auxiliary verb
22	A **B** C D	5/p. 114	Tag questions with *be*
23	A **B** C D	8/p. 120	Reported speech
24	A **B** C D	8/p. 120	Reported speech
25	A B **C** D	8/p. 120	Reported speech
26	**A** B C D	8/p. 120	Reported speech
27	A B **C** D	8/p. 120	Reported speech
28	**A** B C D	6/p. 116	Understand details
29	A **B** C D	6/p. 116	Understand details
30	A B C **D**	6/p. 116	Identify the main idea
31	A B C **D**	6/p. 116	Identify details that support the main idea
32	A B **C** D	9/p. 122	Clearly state a problem
33	**A** B C D	9/p. 122	Clearly ask for a solution to a problem

Please see reverse for test Audio Script.

Unit 6 Test Audio Script

Listening I (Tracks 44–46) Page 40.

1. What are visitors required to do?
   F: Where should I park when I get to your apartment?
   M: Visitors are allowed to park in the lot behind the building. But you have to put a permit on your mirror. I'll give you the permit when you get here.

   What are visitors required to do?

2. What is the landlord going to do?
   F: Hi, this is Tina Brown, your tenant in 2A. I don't have any heat in my apartment. Could you send someone over?
   M: Sure, I'll call someone right now. Will you be at home?
   F: Well, I'm leaving right now, but I'll be back in an hour.

   What is the landlord going to do?

3. What's the problem?
   F: The neighbors' music is so loud that I can't hear our TV! Do you think I should call the building manager?
   M: Yes, you should. I already asked them once to turn it down.

   What's the problem?

Listening II (Tracks 47–48) Page 40.

4. **M:** I can't believe it! The landlord kept our security deposit!
   F: But why? You didn't damage the apartment, did you?

5. **F:** So, do you like my new apartment?
   M: Yes, I think you'll be happy here. How long is your lease?

Listening III (Tracks 49–51) Page 40.

6. **F:** I like this apartment. It would be perfect for me. How much is the rent?
   M: It's $1,100 a month. Water is included. So the tenant just has to pay gas and electric.

   Which sentence is true?

7. **M:** My landlord wants to raise my rent to $900 a month. Is he allowed to do that? I signed a one-year lease, and it'll be up on March 31.
   F: Your lease is still in effect, so the landlord is *not* allowed to raise your rent until after March 31.

   Which sentence is true?

8. **F:** We're not allowed to smoke in our building, but our neighbors smoke in their apartment. I can smell it. I told them we're not allowed to smoke, but they said they didn't care.
   M: You should call the building manager. He can talk to them.
   F: That's a good idea. I'll do that.

   Which sentence is true?

Unit 7 Test Answer Key

	ANSWER	LESSON/PAGE	OBJECTIVE
1	A B **C** D	1/p. 126	Understand a conversation about things to consider when buying a car
2	**A** B C D	1/p. 126	Understand a conversation about things to consider when buying a car
3	A **B** C D	3/p. 130	Understand a conversation about buying car insurance
4	**A** B C D	1/p. 126	Understand a conversation about things to consider when buying a car
5	A **B** C D	5/p. 134	Understand a conversation about car maintenance and repairs
6	A B **C** D	2/p. 128	Understand a conversation about preferences in cars
7	A B **C** D	7/p. 138	Understand a conversation about steps to take after a car accident
8	A B **C** D	7/p. 138	Understand a conversation describing a car accident
9	A B **C** D	3/p. 130	Interpret an auto insurance identification card
10	A **B** C D	3/p. 130	Interpret an auto insurance renewal notice
11	A B **C** D	3/p. 130	Interpret an auto insurance renewal notice
12	A B C **D**	3/p. 130	Interpret an auto insurance renewal notice
13	A B **C** D	2/p. 128	*Would rather* and *would prefer* to express preferences
14	**A** B C D	2/p. 128	*Would rather* and *would prefer* to express preferences
15	**A** B C D	2/p. 128	*Would rather* and *would prefer* to express preferences
16	**A** B C D	2/p. 128	*Would rather* and *would prefer* to express preferences
17	**A** B C D	2/p. 128	*Would rather* and *would prefer* to express preferences
18	A B **C** D	5/p. 134	Embedded *wh-* questions
19	A **B** C D	5/p. 135	Embedded *yes/no* questions
20	A B **C** D	5/p. 134	Embedded *wh-* questions
21	A **B** C D	5/p. 135	Embedded *yes/no* questions
22	A **B** C D	5/p. 134	Embedded *wh-* questions
23	**A** B C D	8/p. 140	Past perfect questions and answers
24	**A** B C D	8/p. 140	Past perfect statements
25	A **B** C D	8/p. 140	Past perfect statements
26	A B **C** D	8/p. 140	Past perfect statements
27	A B **C** D	8/p. 140	Past perfect questions and answers
28	A B C **D**	6/p. 136	Understand details
29	**A** B C D	6/p. 136	Understand details
30	A B C **D**	6/p. 136	Identify the main idea
31	**A** B C D	6/p. 136	Use charts, graphs, and other visuals to learn important facts
32	A **B** C D	9/p. 142	Use time words and phrases to signal steps in a process
33	A B C **D**	9/p. 142	Use time words and phrases to signal steps in a process

Please see reverse for test Audio Script.

Unit 7 Test Audio Script

Listening I (Tracks 52–54) Page 48.

1. What is one feature the man really wants in his car?
    F: So, do you know what features you're looking for in a car?
    M: Yes, I want a two-door compact car with a CD player and air-conditioning. Those things are very important to me. A sunroof would also be nice, but I don't need one.

    What is one feature the man really wants in his car?

2. Who would the man prefer to buy a car from?
    F: I saw an ad for a used car in the paper today. It would be perfect for you. And the guy is selling it for a really good price.
    M: Well, I'd rather buy from a dealer than from an individual. I can get a warranty from a car dealership, but not from a private owner.

    Who would the man prefer to buy a car from?

3. When does the man pay $250?
    F: How much is your monthly insurance premium?
    M: It's $250.

    When does the man pay $250?

Listening II (Tracks 55–56) Page 48.

4. **F:** I'm interested in the white Ford Focus. How many miles are on the car?

5. **F:** Can you take a look at my windshield wipers? I don't know if I need to get new ones.

Listening III (Tracks 57–59) Page 48.

6. **F:** Which car do you like better—the blue two-door or the red four-door?
    M: Well, I'd prefer a four-door car to a two-door. But red isn't my favorite color. I'd rather not get a red car. I think I need to keep looking.

    Which sentence is true?

7. **M:** Are you the woman who called about the car accident?
    F: Yes, officer. I was involved in an accident with another car.
    M: OK. You'll have to fill out an accident report. But first I need to see your driver's license, vehicle registration, and insurance card.

    Which sentence is true?

8. **M:** How did the accident happen?
    F: Well, I put on my turn signal. I had already started moving into the right lane before I saw the other car. The other driver hadn't seen me, either. He had slowed down because of the snow, but there wasn't enough time to stop.

    Which sentence is true?

Unit 8 Test Answer Key

	ANSWER	LESSON/PAGE	OBJECTIVE
1	A B **C** D	5/p. 154	Understand a conversation about ways to reduce your health risks
2	A B **C** D	8/p. 160	Understand a conversation with medical personnel
3	A **B** C D	1/p. 146	Understand a conversation with medical personnel
4	A B **C** D	4/p. 152	Understand a conversation about reporting a medical emergency
5	**A** B C D	2/p. 148	Understand a conversation describing symptoms
6	A B **C** D	7/p. 158	Understand a conversation about preventive health services
7	**A** B C D	1/p. 146	Understand a conversation with medical personnel
8	A B C **D**	6/p. 156	Understand a conversation about preventative health practices
9	A B **C** D	3/p. 150	Interpret a health insurance form
10	A B **C** D	3/p. 150	Interpret a health insurance form
11	A B C **D**	3/p. 150	Interpret a health insurance form
12	A B C **D**	3/p. 150	Interpret a health insurance form
13	A B **C** D	2/p. 148	Present perfect continuous
14	**A** B C D	2/p. 148	Present perfect continuous
15	**A** B C D	2/p. 148	Present perfect continuous
16	A B **C** D	2/p. 148	Present perfect continuous
17	**A** B C D	2/p. 148	Present perfect continuous
18	A **B** C D	5/p. 154	*Such ... that* and *so ... that ...*
19	**A** B C D	5/p. 154	*Such ... that* and *so ... that ...*
20	A B **C** D	5/p. 154	*Such ... that* and *so ... that ...*
21	A B **C** D	5/p. 154	*Such ... that* and *so ... that ...*
22	**A** B C D	5/p. 154	*Such ... that* and *so ... that ...*
23	**A** B C D	8/p. 160	*Should, ought to, had better,* and *must*
24	A **B** C D	8/p. 160	*Should, ought to, had better,* and *must*
25	A **B** C D	8/p. 160	*Should, ought to, had better,* and *must*
26	A B **C** D	8/p. 160	*Should, ought to, had better,* and *must*
27	A B **C** D	8/p. 160	*Should, ought to, had better,* and *must*
28	A B **C** D	6/p. 156	Identify the main idea
29	A B C **D**	6/p. 156	Understand details
30	**A** B C D	6/p. 156	Understand details
31	A B **C** D	6/p. 156	Understand details
32	**A** B C D	9/p. 162	Use sensory details in writing
33	A B C **D**	9/p. 162	Use sensory details in writing

Please see reverse for test Audio Script.

Unit 8 Test Audio Script

Listening I (Tracks 60–61) Page 56.

1. What does the woman say?
   M: I'm trying to help my kids be healthier. I make them healthy meals, and I make sure they get a lot of exercise.
   F: That's great. Make sure that their healthy meals include breakfast every day. It's the most important meal of the day.

   What does the woman say?

2. What is the doctor going to do first?
   F: Dr. Hamm, I feel terrible. I'm tired all the time, and I get stomachaches every day. Do I need to take some medicine?
   M: Well, I'm not sure yet. First I need to examine you and ask you some questions. Then we'll see what you need to do.

   What is the doctor going to do first?

Listening II (Tracks 62–64) Page 56.

3. **M:** Hi, I'm Dr. Cook. What brings you here today?

4. **F:** 911. What's your emergency?
   M: My wife is having trouble breathing.
   F: Is your wife conscious?

5. **F:** So, I hear you're not feeling well.
   M: That's right, doctor.
   F: OK. Tell me about your symptoms.

Listening III (Tracks 65–67) Page 56.

6. **F:** Are you going to the health fair this weekend?
   M: I don't know. Why? Should I go?
   F: Well, they're offering medical checkups for children ages five to eighteen for free. And you can get your child's immunizations for school for just five dollars.

   Which sentence is true?

7. **F:** Here's your prescription. You need to take one tablet daily.
   M: OK. Does the medication have any side effects?
   F: Well, it might cause sleepiness and dry mouth.

   Which sentence is true?

8. **F:** I've decided it's time to lose some weight. I have high blood pressure, and I really need to do something about it.
   M: That's great. You'll improve your health, and you'll feel better, too!

   Which sentence is true?

Unit 9 Test Answer Key

	ANSWER	LESSON/PAGE	OBJECTIVE
1	A Ⓑ C D	2/p. 168	Understand a conversation about parents' involvement in school
2	Ⓐ B C D	1/p. 166	Understand a conversation about a student's progress
3	A B Ⓒ D	1/p. 166	Understand a conversation about a student's progress
4	A Ⓑ C D	4/p. 172	Understand a conversation between parents and school personnel
5	Ⓐ B C D	2/p. 168	Understand a conversation about parents' involvement in school
6	A Ⓑ C D	5/p. 174	Understand a conversation about parents' involvement in school
7	A B Ⓒ D	7/p. 178	Understand a conversation about school safety
8	A Ⓑ C D	4/p. 172	Understand a conversation between parents and school personnel
9	A B C Ⓓ	3/p. 170	Interpret a report card
10	A B Ⓒ D	3/p. 170	Interpret a report card
11	A Ⓑ C D	3/p. 170	Interpret a report card
12	A B Ⓒ D	3/p. 170	Interpret a report card
13	Ⓐ B C D	2/p. 168	Adverb clauses of reason
14	Ⓐ B C D	2/p. 169	Infinitives and adverb clauses of purpose
15	A B Ⓒ D	2/p. 168	Adverb clauses of reason
16	Ⓐ B C D	2/p. 169	Infinitives and adverb clauses of purpose
17	Ⓐ B C D	2/p. 168	Adverb clauses of reason
18	A B Ⓒ D	5/p. 175	Adjective clauses: Relative pronoun as object of the clause
19	A Ⓑ C D	5/p. 174	Adjective clauses: Relative pronoun as subject of the clause
20	Ⓐ B C D	5/p. 174	Adjective clauses: Relative pronoun as subject of the clause
21	A Ⓑ C D	5/p. 175	Adjective clauses: Relative pronoun as object of the clause
22	A B Ⓒ D	5/p. 174	Adjective clauses: Relative pronoun as subject of the clause
23	A Ⓑ C D	8/p. 180	Past modals: Expressing degrees of certainty about the past
24	A B Ⓒ D	8/p. 181	Expressing advice or opinions about the past
25	A Ⓑ C D	8/p. 180	Past modals: Expressing degrees of certainty about the past
26	Ⓐ B C D	8/p. 180	Past modals: Expressing degrees of certainty about the past
27	A B Ⓒ D	8/p. 181	Expressing advice or opinions about the past
28	A Ⓑ C D	6/p. 176	Distinguish fact from opinion
29	A Ⓑ C D	6/p. 176	Distinguish fact from opinion
30	A B Ⓒ D	3/p. 171	Identify the main idea
31	A B C Ⓓ	3/p. 171	Make inferences
32	A B Ⓒ D	9/p. 182	Group similar ideas together in each paragraph
33	A B Ⓒ D	9/p. 182	Group similar ideas together in each paragraph

Please see reverse for test Audio Script.

Unit 9 Test Audio Script

Listening I (Tracks 68–69) Page 64.

1. What does the woman suggest?
   M: I hope the school doesn't cut the after-school programs.
   F: I know. Hey, we should go to the PTA meeting next week and talk to other parents there. We can tell them to talk to school personnel and show support for the after-school programs.
   M: That's a good idea. I think a lot of parents will want to help.

   What does the woman suggest?

2. What did Silvia's teacher recommend for Silvia?
   F: I talked to Silvia's teacher today. She said Silvia always does her homework. But she's having some trouble with math.
   M: So does she need to study more?
   F: Actually, the teacher said it would be good for Silvia to get a tutor.

   What did Silvia's teacher recommend for Silvia?

Listening II (Tracks 70–71) Page 64.

3. **F:** What grade did your daughter get in science?

4. **F:** Do you have proof that you live in this school district?

Listening III (Tracks 72–75) Page 64.

5. **F:** Do you usually go to parent-teacher night?
   M: Yes, I do. It's important for me to know my kids' teachers. I like to know what's going on with them at school.

   Which sentence is true?

6. **F:** Did you go to the PTA meeting last night? I got a note from the school about it. I didn't know what it was, though, so I didn't go.
   M: The PTA is an organization of parents and teachers. They work together to improve schools and student learning.
   F: It sounds good. I should have gone to the meeting.
   M: Don't worry. You can go to next month's meeting.

   Which sentence is true?

7. **F:** The school playground isn't safe. My son said there was a fight on the playground last week.
   M: That's terrible. Someone could have gotten hurt.

   Which sentence is true?

8. **M:** I'd like to talk to my daughter's teacher.
   F: OK. You can talk to her at parent-teacher night, or you can make an appointment for a parent-teacher conference.
   M: I'd like to have a parent-teacher conference. Can we make an appointment for Friday?

   Which sentence is true?

Unit 10 Test Answer Key

	ANSWER	LESSON/PAGE	OBJECTIVE
1	Ⓐ Ⓑ Ⓒ Ⓓ	1/p. 186	Understand a conversation about a progress report
2	Ⓐ Ⓑ Ⓒ Ⓓ	4/p. 192	Understand a conversation about preventing accidents at work
3	Ⓐ Ⓑ Ⓒ Ⓓ	5/p. 194	Understand a conversation about preventing accidents at work
4	Ⓐ Ⓑ Ⓒ Ⓓ	8/p. 200	Understand requests, suggestions, and offers at work
5	Ⓐ Ⓑ Ⓒ Ⓓ	8/p. 200	Understand requests, suggestions, and offers at work
6	Ⓐ Ⓑ Ⓒ Ⓓ	7/p. 198	Understand a conversation about requirements for promotions
7	Ⓐ Ⓑ Ⓒ Ⓓ	2/p. 188	Understand a conversation about work requirements
8	Ⓐ Ⓑ Ⓒ Ⓓ	2/p. 188	Understand a conversation about work requirements
9	Ⓐ Ⓑ Ⓒ Ⓓ	6/p. 196	Interpret an accident report
10	Ⓐ Ⓑ Ⓒ Ⓓ	6/p. 196	Interpret an accident report
11	Ⓐ Ⓑ Ⓒ Ⓓ	6/p. 196	Interpret an accident report
12	Ⓐ Ⓑ Ⓒ Ⓓ	6/p. 196	Interpret an accident report
13	Ⓐ Ⓑ Ⓒ Ⓓ	2/p. 188	*Make/have/let/get* + Verb
14	Ⓐ Ⓑ Ⓒ Ⓓ	2/p. 188	*Make/have/let/get* + Verb
15	Ⓐ Ⓑ Ⓒ Ⓓ	2/p. 188	*Make/have/let/get* + Verb
16	Ⓐ Ⓑ Ⓒ Ⓓ	2/p. 188	*Make/have/let/get* + Verb
17	Ⓐ Ⓑ Ⓒ Ⓓ	2/p. 188	*Make/have/let/get* + Verb
18	Ⓐ Ⓑ Ⓒ Ⓓ	5/p. 194	Reflexive pronouns
19	Ⓐ Ⓑ Ⓒ Ⓓ	5/p. 194	Reflexive pronouns
20	Ⓐ Ⓑ Ⓒ Ⓓ	5/p. 194	Reflexive pronouns
21	Ⓐ Ⓑ Ⓒ Ⓓ	5/p. 194	Reflexive pronouns
22	Ⓐ Ⓑ Ⓒ Ⓓ	5/p. 194	Reflexive pronouns
23	Ⓐ Ⓑ Ⓒ Ⓓ	8/p. 200	*Could you/I … ? / Why don't you/I … ? / Would you mind … ?*
24	Ⓐ Ⓑ Ⓒ Ⓓ	8/p. 200	*Could you/I … ? / Why don't you/I … ? / Would you mind … ?*
25	Ⓐ Ⓑ Ⓒ Ⓓ	8/p. 200	*Could you/I … ? / Why don't you/I … ? / Would you mind … ?*
26	Ⓐ Ⓑ Ⓒ Ⓓ	8/p. 200	*Could you/I … ? / Why don't you/I … ? / Would you mind … ?*
27	Ⓐ Ⓑ Ⓒ Ⓓ	8/p. 200	*Could you/I … ? / Why don't you/I … ? / Would you mind … ?*
28	Ⓐ Ⓑ Ⓒ Ⓓ	3/p. 190	Look for words that signal time order
29	Ⓐ Ⓑ Ⓒ Ⓓ	3/p. 190	Make inferences
30	Ⓐ Ⓑ Ⓒ Ⓓ	3/p. 190	Identify the main idea
31	Ⓐ Ⓑ Ⓒ Ⓓ	3/p. 190	Understand details
32	Ⓐ Ⓑ Ⓒ Ⓓ	9/p. 202	Identify a problem, explain the cause, and suggest a solution
33	Ⓐ Ⓑ Ⓒ Ⓓ	9/p. 202	Identify a problem, explain the cause, and suggest a solution

Please see reverse for test Audio Script.

Unit 10 Test Audio Script

Listening I (Tracks 76–78) Page 72.

1. Why is the man calling?
   M: Hi, Mrs. Lee. I just spoke to John, my subcontractor. He's a little behind schedule because the new door is on back-order. We won't get it until next week.
   F: Can you get the door somewhere else?
   M: We're checking, but so far no one has what we need. But we'll keep looking, and I'll get back to you.

   Why is the man calling?

2. What are the people talking about?
   M: You'd better take off your necklace before you use that machine. It might get caught, and you could get hurt.
   F: Oh, wow! Thanks. I forgot I had it on.
   M: No problem. We have to help keep each other safe.

   What are the people talking about?

3. Who moved the box?
   M: Did you bring this box from the warehouse?
   F: Yes, I did.
   M: OK. You should never lift these big boxes by yourself. They're too heavy for one person.
   F: Thanks, but I didn't do it myself. I got Anna to help me.

   Who moved the box?

Listening II (Tracks 79–80) Page 72.

4. **F:** Hey, David. Can I ask you a favor?
   M: Sure. What is it?
   F: Would you mind helping me move a table?

5. **F:** You've got a lot of work to do.
   M: I know. I'm not sure how I'm going to finish it all.
   F: Well, why don't I help you?

Listening III (Tracks 81–83) Page 72.

6. **F:** I've had my job for four years, and they still haven't promoted me.
   M: Do you know why not? I mean, are you a good employee?
   F: Yes, I'm very efficient, and I'm accurate.
   M: And you get to work on time, don't you?
   F: Well, usually. I try not to be late, but sometimes it's hard!

   Which sentence is true?

7. **M:** Does your boss make you wear a uniform to work?
   F: No. She lets me wear my own clothes.

   Which sentence is true?

8. **F:** What time did you leave work?
   M: Eight. I wanted to stay later to finish more work, but my boss said I had to leave then.

   Which sentence is true?

Unit 11 Test Answer Key

	ANSWER	LESSON/PAGE	OBJECTIVE
1	A B **C** D	1/p. 206	Understand a conversation about misdemeanors
2	**A** B C D	2/p. 208	Understand a conversation about legal problems
3	A **B** C D	2/p. 208	Understand a conversation about legal problems
4	A B **C** D	7/p. 218	Understand a conversation about traffic laws
5	**A** B C D	1/p. 206	Understand a conversation related to misdemeanors
6	A B **C** D	4/p. 212	Understand a conversation about what happens in a courtroom
7	A **B** C D	4/p. 212	Understand a conversation about what happens in a courtroom
8	A B **C** D	7/p. 218	Understand a conversation about traffic laws
9	A B C **D**	3/p. 210	Identify people in a courtroom
10	**A** B C D	3/p. 210	Identify people in a courtroom
11	A B **C** D	3/p. 210	Identify people in a courtroom
12	A B C **D**	3/p. 210	Identify people in a courtroom
13	**A** B C D	2/p. 208	Past continuous for interrupted action
14	A **B** C D	2/p. 208	Past continuous for interrupted action
15	**A** B C D	2/p. 208	Past continuous for interrupted action
16	A **B** C D	2/p. 208	Past continuous for interrupted action
17	A B **C** D	2/p. 208	Past continuous for interrupted action
18	**A** B C D	4/p. 214	Passives: Present passive and simple past passive
19	A **B** C D	5/p. 214	Passives: Present passive and simple past passive
20	A **B** C D	5/p. 214	Passives: Present passive and simple past passive
21	A B **C** D	5/p. 214	Passives: Present passive and simple past passive
22	A B **C** D	5/p. 214	Passives: Present passive and simple past passive
23	**A** B C D	8/p. 220	Adverb clauses of condition and contrast
24	A **B** C D	8/p. 220	Adverb clauses of condition and contrast
25	A B **C** D	8/p. 220	Adverb clauses of condition and contrast
26	A B **C** D	8/p. 220	Adverb clauses of condition and contrast
27	**A** B C D	8/p. 220	Adverb clauses of condition and contrast
28	A B **C** D	6/p. 216	Identify the main idea
29	A B C **D**	6/p. 216	Understand longer sentences
30	A **B** C D	6/p. 216	Understand details
31	A B C **D**	6/p. 216	Make inferences
32	**A** B C D	9/p. 222	Write about different legal systems
33	A **B** C D	9/p. 222	Write about different legal systems

Please see reverse for test Audio Script.

Unit 11 Test Audio Script

Listening I (Tracks 84–86) Page 80.

1. What was the problem?
   F: I heard Gabriela got into some trouble.
   M: Not really. She and some friends were standing in front of a store. Someone dropped some trash on the ground by accident, and the store owner said they were littering.

   What was the problem?

2. Who was identified?
   F: The police think they found the man who robbed the bank downtown.
   M: Really? How did they find him?
   F: He was identified by several people at the crime scene as the robber.

   Who was identified?

3. What happened first?
   F: Sorry I'm late.
   M: No problem. Is everything OK?
   F: Yeah. I was driving here when I saw two people fighting on the street. So I stopped, and I called the police.

   What happened first?

Listening II (Tracks 87–88) Page 80.

4. **F:** I got a ticket last night.
   M: Oh, no. Why did you get it?

5. **F:** Did you know there's a curfew for teenagers in the city?
   M: No, I didn't. Why is there a curfew?

Listening III (Tracks 89–91) Page 80.

6. **M:** Hey, what are you watching?
   F: It's a show about a real court case.
   M: Yeah? What's the case?
   F: A man borrowed money from his brother, but he didn't pay it back. So they went to court, and now a judge is going to decide the case.

   Which sentence is true?

7. **F:** So tell me what happened at the trial.
   M: Edgar Casas was the first witness. He was asked to describe the crime scene. He told the jury what he had seen, and then the lawyer for the defense asked him questions.

   Which sentence is true?

8. **F:** I got a traffic ticket, but it's completely unfair.
   M: Why? What happened?
   F: My car was parked on First Street last Monday. There's a sign that says you can't park there on Mondays. But a tree branch was covering the sign, so I couldn't see it.
   M: It sounds as if you were in the right. You know, you can ask for a trial to contest the ticket.

   Which sentence is true?

Unit 12 Test Answer Key

	ANSWER	LESSON/PAGE	OBJECTIVE
1	(A) B C D	7/p. 238	Understand a conversation about dreams for the future
2	A B (C) D	3/p. 230	Understand a conversation about starting a business
3	A (B) C D	4/p. 232	Understand a conversation about preparing a monthly budget
4	(A) B C D	4/p. 232	Understand a conversation about preparing a monthly budget
5	A B (C) D	1/p. 226	Understand a conversation about bank services
6	(A) B C D	7/p. 238	Understand a conversation about dreams for the future
7	A B (C) D	1/p. 226	Understand a conversation about bank services
8	A B C (D)	4/p. 232	Understand a conversation about preparing a monthly budget
9	(A) B C D	6/p. 236	Interpret an income tax form
10	A (B) C D	6/p. 236	Interpret an income tax form
11	A B C (D)	6/p. 236	Interpret an income tax form
12	A B C (D)	6/p. 236	Interpret an income tax form
13	A B (C) D	2/p. 228	Articles: *a, an, the,* no article (∅)
14	A B (C) D	2/p. 228	Articles: *a, an, the,* no article (∅)
15	A (B) C D	2/p. 228	Articles: *a, an, the,* no article (∅)
16	(A) B C D	2/p. 228	Articles: *a, an, the,* no article (∅)
17	A B (C) D	2/p. 228	Articles: *a, an, the,* no article (∅)
18	(A) B C D	5/p. 234	Future real conditionals
19	(A) B C D	5/p. 234	Future real conditionals
20	A B (C) D	5/p. 234	Future real conditionals
21	A (B) C D	5/p. 234	Future real conditionals
22	(A) B C D	5/p. 234	Future real conditionals
23	A (B) C D	8/p. 240	Present unreal conditionals
24	A B (C) D	8/p. 240	Present unreal conditionals
25	A (B) C D	8/p. 240	Present unreal conditionals
26	(A) B C D	8/p. 240	Present unreal conditionals
27	A B (C) D	8/p. 240	Present unreal conditionals
28	A B (C) D	3/p. 230	Write a summary
29	A B (C) D	3/p. 230	Make inferences
30	A B C (D)	3/p. 230	Identify the main idea
31	A B C (D)	3/p. 230	Understand details
32	A B C (D)	9/p. 242	Use a question and answer to focus a paragraph
33	A (B) C D	9/p. 242	Use a question and answer to focus a paragraph

Please see reverse for test Audio Script.

Unit 12 Test Audio Script

Listening I (Tracks 92–94) Page 88.

1. What would the man do if he had a lot of money?
   F: What would you do if you had a lot of money? Would you quit your job?
   M: Well, I'd quit the job I have now. But I'd get another job. If I didn't work, I'd be bored. If I really had a lot of money, I could work for a charity, and I wouldn't even have to get paid.

   What would the man do if he had a lot of money?

2. What does the man still need to do?
   F: I heard you opened your own restaurant. Congratulations!
   M: Thanks, but it's not official yet. I've gotten all the permits I need, and I've fixed up the building. But I still have to pass some inspections. If I pass those, then I'll officially be able to open the restaurant.

   What does the man still need to do?

3. What is the woman planning to do first?
   M: Do you want to go out tonight?
   F: Sorry, I can't. I'm trying to save some money to go visit my family. If I stop going out so much, I'll have enough money to buy a plane ticket.

   What is the woman planning to do first?

Listening II (Tracks 95–96) Page 88.

4. **M:** I want to make a budget, but I'm not sure where to start.
   F: Well, you should start by listing your regular expenses. For example, what's your biggest monthly expense?

5. **M:** Can you tell me about the Premium Checking Account?
   F: Of course. The account requires a minimum balance of $500, but there's no maintenance fee.
   M: What's the interest rate on that type of account?

Listening III (Tracks 97–99) Page 88.

6. **F:** What would you do if you suddenly got a lot of money?
   M: That's easy. I'd stop working and I'd go to college full time. I've always wanted to get my college degree.

   Which sentence is true?

7. **F:** Can you tell me about the Advantage Checking Account?
   M: Of course. The interest rate on that type of account is 1 percent. The minimum balance is $1,000.
   F: And are there any fees?
   M: Only if your balance falls below the minimum.

   Which sentence is true?

8. **F:** Do you have any debt?
   M: Yes. I have about $1,000 in credit card debt.
   F: And how much are you paying each month?
   M: $50.

   Which sentence is true?

Life Skills (Track 27) Page 18.

9. What are the center's hours?

   M: When could my son take classes at the center?

   F: Well, they open right after school—at 3:30—and the last class ends at 7:00 P.M.

   What are the center's hours?

10. What are the center's fees?

   F: How much do activities at the community center cost?

   M: There are no fees. You don't have to pay for any of their activities.

   What are the center's fees?

11. What should the woman do?

   F: Can you give me directions to the park?

   M: Sure. First go north on Orchard Street. Then make a left and go west on Bruce Avenue for about a mile.

   F: OK. North on Orchard, west on Bruce. Got it. Thanks.

   What should the woman do?

12. Where is the community center?

   M: It's easy to get to the community center. Make a right at the corner, and go east on Sterling Street for about two miles. The address is 406 Sterling Street.

   F: What's the nearest cross street?

   M: It's Amber Drive.

   Where is the community center?

To use the *Future* **Exam**_View_® *Assessment Suite*, your computer must meet or exceed the following requirements:

For Windows®:
- Intel Pentium® II 120 MHz or compatible processor
- Microsoft Windows® 2000/XP/Vista

For Macintosh®:
- Power PC® 120 MHz or higher processor
- Mac OS X (10.2 or later)

Both:
- 100 MB of available hard drive space
- 128 MB of available RAM (256 MB recommended)
- Monitor capable of displaying 16-bit color with 800 x 600 resolution
- Internet connection to access test-hosting features, and for Content Update Feature
- CD-ROM Drive

These instructions are for **Exam**_View Test Generator_ version 6. If you have an earlier version of **Exam**_View_ installed on your computer, it will automatically be replaced by this version when you install it. You can then create all your new tests in this version. If you open an existing test or question bank created with the earlier version, it will automatically be updated.

For Windows®:
1. Close all other programs before you begin the installation.
2. Insert the **Exam**_View_ disc into the CD-ROM drive of your computer.
3. You may be prompted by the computer to open the disc. If this doesn't happen, open **My Computer**.
4. Double-click on the CD-ROM drive icon.

5. Double click on the TO THE TEACHER document in order to read it. This document will instruct you in the best practices to use the *Future* **Exam**_View Assessment Suite_ products. The document will also provide instructions for using the listening portions of the *Future* **Exam**_View_ tests.
6. After closing the TO THE TEACHER document, double click on the **SETUP** file and follow the instructions on the screen.
7. When the installation is complete, remove the **Exam**_View_ disc from the CD-ROM drive of your computer.

For Macintosh®:
1. Close all other programs before you begin the installation.
2. Insert the **Exam**_View_ disc into the CD-ROM drive of your computer.
3. Double-click on the **Exam**_View_ icon that appears on the desktop.
4. Double click on the TO THE TEACHER document in order to read it. This document will instruct you in the best practices to use the *Future* **Exam**_View Assessment Suite_ products. The document will also provide instructions for using the listening portions of the *Future* **Exam**_View_ tests.
5. After closing the TO THE TEACHER document, double click on the **Exam**_View_ installer icon and follow the instructions on the screen.
6. When installation is complete, remove the **Exam**_View_ disc from the CD-ROM drive of your computer.

ISBN-13: 978-0-13-240919-3
ISBN-10: 0-13-240919-4